Philip Kerr

Inside Out

Workbook

MACMILLAN

Macmillan Education
Between Towns Road, Oxford OX4 3PP, UK
A division of Macmillan Publishers Limited
Companies and representatives throughout the world
ISBN 0 333 75755 6 (International Edition)
ISBN 0 333 96737 2 (Level III)

Designed by Jackie Hill at 320 Design
Illustrated by Katie Atkin pp26, 27; Peter Campbell pp14, Paul
Collicut pp22, 39, 50, 78; David Hopkins p61; Julian Mosedale pp18, 30,
49, 59, 65, 69, 70, 72, 74, 76; Gary Rees pp24, 45, 66.
Cover design by Andrew Oliver
Cover illustration © Howard Hodgkin

The author and publishers would like to thank the following for
permission to reproduce copyright material: Penguin Books
Australia for the extracts on p10 from *The Little Book of Calm* by Paul
Wilson; Random House Group and Sheil Land Associates for the
extracts on p10 from *The Little Book of Stress* by Rohan Candappa,
published by Ebury Press 1998 © Rohan Candappa 1998; Macmillan
Heinemann ELT and Random House for the extract on p12 from
Jurassic Park by Michael Crichton, and Macmillan Heinemann ELT
for the extracts on p12 from *Oliver Twist* by Charles Dickens and *The
Woman Who Disappeared* by Philip Prowse and the extract on p18
adapted from *The Great Gatsby* by F. Scott Fitzgerald, all in the
Heinemann Guided Reader series; the dictionary extracts on p21 are
reproduced from Collins COBUILD Dictionary with the permission
of HarperCollins Publishers Ltd, © HarperCollins Publishers 1995:
Updated from the Bank of English. Based on the COBUILD series,
developed in collaboration with the University of Birmingham.
COBUILD® and Bank of English® are registered trademarks of
HarperCollins Publishers Ltd; the poem on p30 is from BIG BAD
RAPS by Tony Mitton first published in the UK by Orchard Books in
1996, a division of The Watts Publishing Group Limited, 96 Leonard
Street, London EC2A 4XD; the extracts on p32 are reprinted with
permission from *The Week* magazine; the extract on p7 was adapted
from The Brand New Heavies web site at www.dvinyl.com; the
jokes on p74 were taken from *The Penguin Dictionary of Jokes*
compiled by Fred Metcalf.

The authors and the publishers would like to thank the
following for permission to reproduce their material:
Image Bank p73; Penguin p11; Popperfoto p25; Rex p48;
Stone p29

The cartoons on p26 are from SUPERKID HANDBOOK © 1994
Laurence Anholt. Illustrations © 1994 Martin Chatterton.
Reproduced by permission of the publisher Walker Books Ltd.,
London.

Printed and bound in Spain by Edelvives SA

2004 2003
10 9 8 7 6

Contents

1 Friends

English expressions

1 Arrange the words below to make well-known English expressions about friendship.

a) *friend girl's a best are diamonds*

_____

b) *friends enemies like who that with needs ?*

_____

c) *friend friend need a a is in indeed*

_____

2 Do you have similar expressions in your language? Write them in the space provided.

_____

_____

_____

Grammar

TONIGHT'S TV CHOICE
Channel 4: 10 pm

★★★★★ Friends

The series ends with Ross getting married to Emily, but it is clear that he is thinking about Rachel. During the party afterwards, Emily disappears and her father is drunk. Monica is having an affair with Chandler. She goes back to New York with Joey to see Phoebe, who is pregnant. Ross goes to the airport for his honeymoon alone. There, he meets Rachel and invites her to join him on his honeymoon. Then Emily arrives. Ross has to decide between the two women. Rachel finally takes the plane – alone, but there is just a chance that Ross joins her.

1 First, read the review of the television series *Friends* and complete the questions with a word from the box. One question does not need a question word.

Then match the questions to the correct answer from the list below.

What	When	Where	Who	Whose
Why	How			

Example
How does the series end? **4**

a) _____ does Emily disappear? ☐

b) _____ father gets drunk? ☐

c) _____ is having an affair with Monica?
☐

d) _____ do Monica and Joey go? ☐

e) _____ do Monica and Joey want to see
Phoebe? ☐

f) _____ does Ross ask Rachel to do?
☐

g) _____ does Ross go with Rachel? ☐

1 Chandler.   5 She's pregnant.
2 During the party. 6 New York.
3 Go with him.   7 We don't know.
4 With Ross's wedding. 8 Emily's.

2 Complete the questions with a preposition from the box. Two of the questions do not need a preposition.

about	between	to	to	with	with

a) How did the series end _____?
b) What did the series end _____?
c) Who did Ross get married _____?
d) Who was Ross thinking _____?
e) Who was Monica having an affair _____?
f) Which city did Monica go back _____?
g) Who did Rachel meet at the airport _____?
h) Who did Ross have to decide _____?

3 Circle the correct verb form.

A: (a) *Did you see / Saw you* 'Friends' on TV last night?

B: Why? Did anything special (b) *happen/ happened*?

A: Well, you remember that Rachel got angry with Ross when they were playing cards?

B: Yes ...

A: Well, the next day he invited her out to dinner ...

B: What (c) *did happen / happened*?

A: She was just telling him that she wanted to be with someone else when, in through the door ...

B: ... his ex-wife arrived!

A: No!

B: Who (d) *was it / did it be*? Her boyfriend?

A: No, it was Chandler and the others.

B: Oh no! What (e) *did they want / they wanted*?

A: Well, it was quite funny – no, I tell you what, I'll lend you the video.

4 📼 Look at the questions in the dialogue in Exercise 3 again and underline the strongest stress in each question. Then listen to the recording to check your answers. Practise saying the questions.

5 All of the questions below contain a grammatical mistake. Correct the mistake and answer the questions.

1 How many times do you can fold a piece of paper?
a) 7   b) 9   c) 13

2 Who was the first CD in the US recorded?
a) The Rolling Stones   b) Michael Jackson
c) Bruce Springsteen

3 How much lipstick uses the average woman in her lifetime?
a) 0.5 kg   b) 1.5 kg   c) 2.5 kg

4 Which singer did the Wailers play?
a) Celine Dion   b) Bob Marley
c) Elvis Presley

5 How much weighs your brain?
a) 1.5 kg   b) 2.5 kg   c) 3.5 kg

6 Who's real name is Annie Mae Bullock?
a) Madonna   b) Tina Turner
c) Celine Dion

7 How many birthdays does the Queen of England have got?
a) 1   b) 2   c) 3

8 Which companies did make the first CD?
a) Philips and Sony   b) EMI and Island
c) Virgin and Polygram

9 Whose countries was the shortest war in history between?
a) England and Scotland
b) Israel and Egypt
c) England and Zanzibar

10 Which country did win the first World Cup?
a) Brazil   b) Uruguay   c) Argentina

6 Rearrange the words to make questions.

a) to   married   Lennon   was   who
John

_____

b) John   killed   Lennon   was   when

_____

c) does   Keith   Richards   songs   who
with   write

_____

d) and   common   got   have   in
The Brand New Heavies   what
Carole King

_____

_____

e) mother   Nicaragua   from   whose
came

_____

f) singer   *Je ne regrette rien*   French
made   which   famous

_____

_____

Now answer the questions. The answers are all in Unit 1 of your coursebook.

a) _____

b) _____

c) _____

d) _____

e) _____

f) _____

_____

7 Complete the sentences by putting the verb in brackets in the correct form.

Examples
Who (kill) John Lennon? – Mark Chapman.
Who killed John Lennon?
Who (shoot) Mark Chapman? – John Lennon.
Who did Mark Chapman shoot?

a) Which company (buy) Rolls Royce in 1998? – Volkswagen.

_____

_____

b) Which song (sing) Elton John at Princess Diana's funeral? – Candle in the Wind.

_____

_____

c) Who (train) Aranxta Sanchez? – Her father.

_____

_____

d) Who (play) Madonna in the film Evita? – The title role.

_____

_____

e) What opera (write) Verdi in 1853? – La Traviata.

_____

_____

Pronunciation

1 📼 In the following groups of words, three words have short vowels underlined and three have long. Group the words in the appropriate boxes. Then listen to the recording to check your answers and practise saying the words.

a) army, father, perhaps, salary, start, thank

short /æ/	long /ɑ:/

b) because, called, common, fall, model, noughts

short /ɒ/	long /ɔ:/

c) dream, killed, lived, people, ski, women

short /ɪ/	long /i:/

d) dead, earn, first, friend, hurt, rest

short /e/	long /ɜ:/

2 Now decide if the following underlined vowel sounds are long or short. Use a dictionary to check your answers.

a) coffee
b) father
c) fished
d) happy
e) head
f) heard
g) receive
h) sorts

3 Match the words in each column which have the same vowel sounds.

night	earn	truth
born	choose	come
hurt	chose	fall
soul	alive	smoke
whose	love	eye
won	nought	world

4 Look at the underlined prepositions in the following pairs of sentences. Decide if the prepositions should be pronounced in the strong form (eg /frɒm/) or the weak form (eg /frəm/).

Example
Where does she come from? *strong*
She comes from Little Rock. *weak*

a) What did you do that for?
I did it for you!

b) Who did you send the letter to?
I sent it to the director.

c) What are you looking at?
I'm looking at the instructions.

d) What were you thinking of?
I was thinking of the day we met.

📼 Listen to the recording to check your answers and practise saying the sentences.

Reading

The Brand New Heavies

Growing up in the London suburb of Ealing, old school friends Jan Kincaid, Andrew Levy and Simon Bartholomew pursued their love of soul music and 70s funk in the London clubs of the mid-eighties. They listened and danced to the music of James Brown, The Crusaders, Rufus and many others, and decided they had no option but to try it for themselves. They rehearsed regularly at Kincaid's home and, under the name of Brothers International, recorded their music on tape. When local DJs started playing their music after a James Brown track, they were ecstatic.

In 1987, when they renamed themselves The Brand New Heavies, they added a brass section, and their debut album was released on the indie label, Acid Jazz. This recording captured the attention of Michael Ross, founder of the Los Angeles-based label Delicious Vinyl, and in 1990, Ross signed the Heavies to his label and paired them with Atlanta-born vocalist N'Dea Davenport. He sent them back into the studio to re-record several songs and add some new ones. When the band made their US debut, *Never Stop* became a Top 5 R & B single, and they haven't stopped since. Meanwhile, back in the UK, songs like *Dream Come True* and *Stay This Way* invaded the airwaves, transforming the band from a club wonder into a world-wide success.

In 1992, the band started working with hip hop artists like Masta Ace and Kool G. Rap, and their second release broke all the rules by mixing rap with their own style of funk. The next album, *Brother Sister* produced a string of hits and went double platinum in the UK and near gold in the US. At this point N'Dea Davenport left the group to go solo, and the vocalist/songwriter, Siedah Garrett, who had worked with Quincy Jones, Michael Jackson and Madonna, joined up. Together, they recorded *Shelter*, their most successful disc to date. The title track is a hard piece of funk with a disco feel, there is also an instrumental and beautiful ballads like *Feels Like Right*.

No longer just an acid jazz band, we can expect more changes in the future. Says Andrew Levy, 'The Brand New Heavies are still kicking, no doubt about it. We're moving on and we're moving on strong.'

1 Read the article about The Brand New Heavies and mark the statements below T (true) or F (false).

a) James Brown made soul music. ☐

b) Their music was played in discos. ☐

c) Their first success was in the UK. ☐

d) *Brother Sister* did not sell very well. ☐

e) Davenport was replaced by Siedah Garrett. ☐

f) They worked with Michael Jackson. ☐

g) The song *Shelter* is a ballad. ☐

h) The Brand New Heavies always use the same musical style. ☐

2 Read through the text and find 6 more words that describe different forms of *recorded music*, and 9 words that describe *kinds of music*.

recorded music

> *track*

kinds of music

3 Find words or expressions in the text that mean the same as:

Paragraph 1
a) choice
b) practised
c) very happy

Paragraph 2
d) first
e) creator
f) was played on the radio

Paragraph 3
g) many
h) independent
i) so far

Vocabulary

1 Complete the text below with the expressions in the box.

```
drift apart
ended up
get back together
split up
getting on
going out
gone our separate ways
had a lot in common
hit it off
missed her
started seeing
were very close
```

People often ask me why Charlotte and I
(a) _____ , although this wasn't
the first time we had (b) _____
_____ . When I first met her, we really
(c) _____ . We (d) _____
_____ and started going out
and soon we (e) _____ .
Then I had to go to America for my job and we
began to (f) _____ . When she
called me and said she didn't want a
long-distance relationship I wasn't really
surprised. In any case, I had already
(g) _____ someone else.
A few months after I came back we started
(h) _____ again. We were
(i) _____ really well and I realised
how much I had (j) _____ . She
told me how important it was to share everything
about our lives and I (k) _____
telling her about the girl I had met in the States. I
told her that it hadn't been serious, but she got
really angry and said I was just a typical man!
That was the beginning of the end, but I still hope
that one day we'll (l) _____ .

2 Combine the word *friend* with the prefix and suffixes in the box to make ...

... 3 adjectives
_____

... 3 nouns
_____

```
              less
 un   friend  ly
              ness
              ship
```

3 Match the words on the left to the words on the right to make phrases. Then complete the sentences below with these phrases.

answer	a company
appear in	a film
earn	a flat
play for	friends
make	a good salary
join	the party
share	the phone
tell	a team
work for	the truth

Example
Could you *answer the phone*? I'm busy.

a) After leaving Italy, Maradona went to
_____
in Argentina.

b) I didn't _____ about
where I went last night.

c) I used to live on my own but now I
_____ with two
friends.

d) My job isn't very interesting, but I
_____ .

e) She decided to _____
after the last election.

f) She's going to _____
with Leonardo DiCaprio.

g) When I finish my studies, I'm hoping to
_____ where
I can use my English.

h) When I went to live in the capital, I found it
difficult at first to _____ .

Writing

1 The following e-mail messages were sent to a magazine for English language students. Which messages would you like to reply to?

2 Each message contains two spelling mistakes and one mistake of grammar. Find the errors and correct them.

3 Choose three of the messages and write short replies to them.

I can't understand English TV. I think that watching TV is a good way to improove my English, but I can't understand most programmes. Does anyone knows a satelite or cable programme that is good for intermediate students? Nothing boring, please!

Andrej, Poland

MUSIC! MUSIC! MUSIC!
Sing and learn English! Do you want to echange English song lyrics? Tell me what you're into and we'll see if our taistes match. What does interests you?

Valentina, Italy

I speak a little English but I want to start classes at a langauge school. There are hundreds of schools in my city and I don't know how to chose! What should I look for? What sort of questions you would ask?

Waldemar, Brazil

Hi! My name's Natalia. I'm thinking of going to America or Britian next autum for an English language course. How I start looking for a good school? Can anyone help me?

Natalia, Argentina

HELP! I've got an English exam next month and my grammer is not so good. Who does know a good English textbook with practice exersises? Who publishes it?

Markus, Switzerland

PS I've got the blue book and I've finished it already.

2 Relax

Useful tips(!)

The Little Book of Calm gives short pieces of advice for the stressed reader. Another book, *The Little Book of Stress*, tells you how you can become more stressed! Which of these pieces of advice come from *The Little Book of Calm* and which come from *The Little Book of Stress*?

a) Choose friends you don't like.

b) Take the time to brush someone's hair. Better still, brush your own – or have someone else do it.

c) Eat more fruit and vegetables.

d) Do the weekly shopping in a big supermarket on a Saturday morning. Take your children with you. If you haven't any children of your own, borrow some.

e) When going anywhere, make sure you set off late. Especially if you're going to an important appointment.

f) Wear white. The clothes you wear have a distinct influence on the way you feel.

g) Write down your worries. Read the list before you go to bed.

h) A double espresso just before bed is always a winner.

Grammar

1 In the following sentences, the adverbs of frequency are in the wrong place. Make the corrections.

a) I have time to rarely read novels these days.

_____

_____

b) I normally am too tired in the evenings to do anything except watch TV.

_____

_____

c) People give me books at Christmas often and I like to read them in the holidays.

_____

_____

d) People in Britain read frequently the newspaper while they are having breakfast.

_____

_____

e) My boyfriend reads the newspaper always on the way to work, but he usually just looks at the sports pages.

_____

_____

f) My boyfriend and I go normally to the cinema twice a month, but sometimes we go every week.

_____

_____

g) Hardly ever we eat in restaurants, but we often get a take-away Chinese meal.

_____

_____

h) Usually on a Saturday morning, once a month, I take the children to the cinema.

_____

_____

2 Complete the sentences with a verb from the box using either the present simple or the present continuous.

do	get	eat	look	love	take
think	try				

a) Paul is a manager and _____ his job, but he is worried about its effect on his health.

b) He _____ for a new job that is less stressful.

c) He _____ to manage his time better so that he isn't so stressed all the time.

d) He makes sure that he _____ at least eight hours sleep every night.

e) The journey to work _____ one hour and he's decided to use this time for relaxation.

f) He has stopped having sandwiches for lunch and now _____ a proper meal every day.

g) He always _____ some kind of sport twice a week.

h) He _____ about taking up yoga, but he hasn't made up his mind yet.

3 Complete the sentences with an auxiliary verb from the box.

do	does	are	is	has	have

Example
do
I ⅄ not usually walk to work.

a) How often ___ you look at yourself in the mirror?

b) I never ___ had a massage.

c) It's the best film I ___ ever seen.

d) She ___ already got too many appointments.

e) She ___ not need another appointment to worry about.

f) The book ___ sold over two million copies so far.

g) When one child ___ screaming, I don't feel calm.

h) ___ you reading anything interesting?

4 Match the questions in box A with their answers in box B.

A

| a) Do you smoke? |
| b) Have you seen Sue and James lately? |
| c) How often do you go to the cinema? |
| d) You've changed, haven't you? |
| e) Your English is getting worse, isn't it? |
| f) What are you reading at the moment? |

B

| 1 Hardly ever. I haven't been for ages. |
| 2 Nothing. I've just finished something. |
| 3 To be honest, I don't love you any more. |
| 4 Yes, but I'm trying to give up. |
| 5 Yes, I'm staying with them at the moment. |
| 6 Yes. I never use it. |

5 Circle the correct tense.

Death of a Salesman by Arthur Miller
This is the story of Willy Loman, an unsuccessful salesman who (a) *is getting / gets* old. His wife, Linda, (b) *is always supporting / has always supported* him, but his son, Biff, (c) *is not believing / does not believe* in his father's dreams. Willy (d) *wants / has wanted* to start a new business, but recently Biff (e) *starts / has started* to think about leaving home, and he (f) *is not wanting / does not want* to help his father. Willy is so depressed that he (g) *already starts / has already started* to think about suicide. At the moment, he (h) *is finding / finds* it harder and harder to believe that he can help his family.

6 Complete the spaces in the text below with an appropriate form of the verb in brackets. Use the present simple, present continuous or present perfect.

Paul Wilson

Paul Wilson, author of *The Little Book of Calm*, not only writes books. He also
(a) _____ (work) for an advertising agency and is the director of a hospital. From time to time, he also (b) _____ (produce) musical albums and he frequently (c) _____ (give) talks to business people. Because of, or despite, this busy life, he
(d) _____ (become) a world authority on calm. He (e) _____ _____ (already publish) two novels and many books on the subject of calm. In the last few years, he (f) _____ (sell) more than any other Australian writer. So far, his work (g) _____ (appear) in over twelve languages, and this number
(h) _____ (increase). As a result, he (i) _____ (become) very famous around the world. National newspapers regularly (j) _____ (write) articles about him and, at least once a month, there is a TV programme which discusses his work. At the moment, he
(k) _____ (work) on a number of new projects and, at the same time,
(l) _____ (try) to find time to spend with his three children.

Listening and reading

1   Read the descriptions of three novels and match them to the book covers.

a)   Taken from the most famous movie of all time, this is the story of a theme park where visitors come face to face with living, breathing dinosaurs … for the first time in 64 million years.

b)   Dickens' famous novel about a poor orphan boy who runs away to London and finds himself in the criminal underworld of the city.

c)   An amusing story of the adventures of a Los Angeles private detective. A beautiful blonde woman hires Lenny Samuel to find her missing sister. Before long the stage also contains gunmen, dead bodies, policemen and jewel thieves.

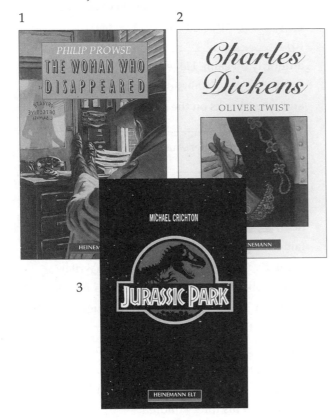

1

2

3

2   📼   Cover the texts opposite. Listen to three extracts from the above novels and say which novel each extract comes from. (If you don't have the recording, read the extracts.)

3   📼   The following words are missing from the extracts opposite. Read the extracts and decide where they should go. (They are given in the correct order.) Then listen to the recording again to check your answers.

Extract 1:   by   at   away   onto   against

Extract 2:   by   in   with   out of   towards

Extract 3:   on   in   in   of   round

1

Just then, the door opened behind me. Jo and his tall friend stood in the doorway, and the tall man was holding a gun. There was a loud bang as the gun went off. The bang was followed a scream of pain from one of the cooks, because the tall man had shot him in the foot by mistake. I quickly picked up a large pile of dirty plates and threw them Jo. He saw the plates coming and he tried to move. As he moved, he slipped on the floor and fell a pile of broken plates.

Without waiting, I ran to a door at the back of the kitchen. The door was locked and I banged it with my shoulder. The lock broke easily and I pushed the door open. As I ran out into the dark street, I could still hear the shouts and cries coming from the Club.

2

As they walked, they heard the roar of an animal. The hadrosaurs the lake were suddenly worried. They started to run and cry out fear. Then, a terrible roar, the adult rex ran the trees by the lake. It chased the hadrosaurs. Grant, Lex and Tim ran some rocks and started to climb them. The ground shook. The huge, five-tonne hadrosaurs ran round them, crashing and trumpeting. Grant waited till the hadrosaurs had run past. Then he made the children climb the nearest tree. They could hide there until he was sure the tyrannosaur had gone.

3

The old gentleman went reading. He had grey hair and wore gold spectacles. He wore a long, dark green coat and white trousers. The Dodger moved nearer. The next moment, the old gentleman's silk handkerchief was the Dodger's hand. The Dodger and Charley ran and hid the doorway a house. The old gentleman touched his pocket. He turned quickly. 'That boy's got my handkerchief!' he cried.

Vocabulary

1 Complete the adjectives in column A with *–ed* or *–ing*. Then complete the sentences with a phrase from column B.

A

a) When I am depress_____

b) If people are confus_____

c) It was a depress_____ film

d) I get quite annoy_____

e) Some people find it very relax_____

f) It was the most embarrass_____ experience

g) I was so tir_____

h) He was so excit_____

i) My job is very bor_____

j) We thought it would be more interest_____

B

1 and I wish I hadn't gone to see it.

2 I decided to have a short nap.

3 I have ever had.

4 I often get headaches.

5 so I'm looking for another one.

6 they sometimes scratch their head.

7 that he talked non-stop.

8 to have a leisurely hot bath.

9 to take a different route.

10 with people who can't stop fidgeting.

2 Complete these sentences with a preposition from the box.

about	by	for	for	from	in
in	into	into	on	over	under

a) The book is divided _____ short pieces of advice.

b) It has made its author _____ a multi-millionaire.

c) It has sold _____ two million copies.

d) A relaxed person regularly goes _____ a walk.

e) I was _____ the impression that I was a relaxed sort of person.

f) I judge a book _____ its cover.

g) It's a film based _____ a book by Nicholas Evans.

h) Grace is involved _____ an appalling riding accident.

i) Her only hope lies _____ Booker, a rancher from Montana.

j) Booker is a man with a special talent _____ healing horses.

k) Nothing much happens apart _____ an accident with a horse.

l) There is no doubt _____ the fact that he is a competent director.

3 Which films are examples of the following types?

a) Cartoons ☐

b) Gangster films ☐

c) Horror films ☐

d) Love stories ☐

e) Romantic comedies ☐

f) Science fiction films ☐

g) Thrillers ☐

h) War films ☐

i) Westerns ☐

1 *The Godfather*
Scarface
Goodfellas

2 *Star Wars*
Star Trek
Close Encounters of the Third Kind

3 *Four Weddings and a Funeral*
Notting Hill
Green Card

4 *Shakespeare In Love*
Romeo and Juliet
Pretty Woman

5 *Nightmare on Elm Street*
The Exorcist
Friday the Thirteenth

6 *The Magnificent Seven*
Dances With Wolves
The Last of the Mohicans

7 *Silence of the Lambs*
The Client
Witness

8 *The Lion King*
Aladdin
Beauty and the Beast

9 *Saving Private Ryan*
Rambo
Apocalypse Now

Writing

1 An English-language magazine wants you to write an article about how people of your age spend their spare time in your area.
First look at the activities illustrated below and tick the things that are particularly popular with people in your area. If there are other popular activities that are not shown, add them.

2 Choose the three or four most popular activities. Decide why you think these are so popular.

3 Do people generally spend their spare time alone, with a group of friends or with just one friend?

4 Which activities do people choose to do when they are short of money? And when money is not a problem?

5 Complete these sentences:

In the summer, people tend to _____ but in the winter months _____ .

Not everyone enjoys _____ so _____ _____ .

In recent years, people have started to _____ _____ .

6 Make a short plan for your article. Organise your ideas into four paragraphs. Think about adverbs of frequency and decide which of these you could use.

7 Write an article of between 120 and 180 words.

3 Dating

Quotations

1 Complete the sentences below with a word from the box.

> boyfriends   experience   face   kiss
> love   marriage   youth

a) There were three of us in the _____ , so it was a bit crowded.

b) I gave my beauty and my _____ to men. I am going to give my wisdom and _____ to animals.

c) I still remember the chewing gum, tobacco and beer taste of my first _____ , exactly 40 years ago, although I have completely forgotten the _____ of the American sailor who kissed me.

d) If grass can grow through cement, _____ can find you at every time in your life.

e) I make my _____ famous.

2 Now match the quotations above to these famous women:

1 Isabelle Allende
2 Brigitte Bardot
3 Naomi Campbell
4 Cher
5 Princess Diana

Grammar

1 Read the letter opposite, which was written to an 'agony aunt' in a magazine, and choose the best summary of the writer's problems.

a) Vincent is in love with a Japanese girl who is not in love with him.

b) Vincent is sad because his girlfriend has gone back to Japan.

c) Vincent cannot express his feelings when he is with the girl he loves.

d) Vincent is sad because he has lost his umbrella.

Dear Margaret,

I first met Chiyo, a Japanese girl, about six months ago. It was at a party and she gave me a lift home in her car. I really liked her, but I was so nervous that I couldn't think of anything to say.

The next day, I rang her to ask her out, but when she picked up the phone, I got scared and said something stupid about leaving my umbrella in her car instead.

Since that time, I've met her three or four times, always with a group of friends, but I've always been too shy to say anything. Now I have just found out that she has gone back to Japan. One of her friends told me – she left on Tuesday. Now that she has gone, I've really started missing her. Every day I sit down and try to write a letter to tell Chiyo how I feel about her, but every time I start I cannot find the right words. Can you help me?

Yours,
Vincent

---

2 Look again at the letter from Vincent. Underline all the verbs that are in the past simple and circle the verbs that are in the present perfect. Then use those verbs to help you complete the table below.

infinitive	past simple	past participle
be	_____	_____
find	_____	_____
get	_____	_____
give	_____	_____
leave	_____	_____
meet	_____	_____
ring	_____	_____
say	_____	_____
see	_____	_____

3 Circle the correct form of the verb.

A: You look happy, Chiyo! What's up?

C: Yeah, guess what? I (a) *meet / 've met* a guy I really like.

A: When was this? At the party last Saturday?

C: Uh-huh. I (b) *have given / gave* him a lift home in my car. He's really shy, but I (c) *think / have thought* he liked me, too.

A: (d) *Have you seen / Did you see* him since the party? (e) *Does he telephone / Has he telephoned* you in the last few days?

C: Yes, he (f) *has called / called* on Monday, but he (g) *hasn't said / didn't say* anything special.

A: So, why (h) *do you think / have you thought* that he's interested in you?

C: I (i) *see / 've seen* him a few times – you know, with friends around town, and it's the way he went red every time he (j) *has seen / saw* me! He's really cute!

4 Complete the sentences below with *for* or *since*.

a) She's only known him _____ about six weeks.

b) I've been in love with you _____ the day we met.

c) They have been together _____ the beginning of the year.

d) They've only been engaged _____ a couple of weeks.

e) He hasn't had a girlfriend _____ Anna left him.

f) She's fancied him _____ months and months.

g) They've been friends _____ they were little children.

h) They haven't been married _____ very long.

5 Complete the sentences using a verb from the box in the past simple or present perfect and *for*, *since* or *ago*.

be	fall	have	know	see	speak
tell	try	wait	want		

Example
Vincent first /_____/ to Chiyo / six months
Vincent first spoke to Chiyo six months ago.

a) Vincent /_____/ Chiyo / about six months

_____

_____

b) Vincent /_____/ in love with Chiyo / six months

_____

_____

c) Chiyo /_____/ Vincent's umbrella / the party

_____

_____

d) Vincent /_____/ to ask Chiyo out / she took him home

_____

_____

e) Vincent /_____/ Chiyo a number of times / he first met her

_____

_____

f) One of Chiyo's friends /_____/ Vincent about her departure for Japan / a week

_____

_____

g) Chiyo /_____/ in Japan / Tuesday

_____

_____

h) Vincent /_____/ to write to Chiyo / a few days

_____

_____

i) Chiyo /_____/ for Vincent to ask her out / six months

_____

_____

6 Answer the following questions about yourself.

a) How long have you known your best friend?

_____

b) How long have you lived in your present home?

_____

c) How long have you studied English?

_____

d) How long have you had this book?

_____

e) How long have you spent on this exercise?

_____

7 Rewrite your answers to the questions in Exercise 6 using the past simple. You will often need to change the verb that you use.

Example
How long have you known your best friend?
(I have known her) for six years.

I met her six years ago.

a) _____

_____

_____

b) _____

_____

_____

c) _____

_____

_____

d) _____

_____

_____

Pronunciation

1 📼 Look at these words which all end in *–ed*. How many syllables does each word have? One or two? Listen to the recording and practise saying them.

Example
asked 1   crowded 2

a) ended   e) liked   i) tried
b) hated   f) needed   j) waited
c) helped   g) scared   k) wanted
d) kissed   h) stressed   l) thanked

What do the words with two syllables have in common?

2 Rewrite these sentences so that the verb is contracted. Then circle the preposition(s) in each sentence that will be pronounced with a /ə/.

Example
I have not spoken to him for ages.

I haven't spoken to him (for) ages.

a) I have always wanted to go to Bali.

_____

b) She has been married for nearly a month.

_____

c) It was not love at first sight.

_____

d) She has known him for a couple of years.

_____

e) We did not learn from our mistakes.

_____

f) She has always had a strong sense of family.

_____

g) Did you not see Jack at the weekend?

_____

📼 Listen to the sentences and practise saying them.

3 📼 Listen to the following sentences and underline the word which is stressed.

a) He isn't exactly patient.
b) She isn't particularly sensitive.
c) They're not what you'd call intelligent.
d) He isn't especially hard-working.
e) She's not very generous.
f) They're not exactly open-minded.

Listen again and practise saying the sentences.

Listening and reading

1 [cassette icon] Cover the tapescript opposite and listen to a dialogue from *The Great Gatsby* by F. Scott Fitzgerald. Which picture best illustrates the scene?

2 Now read the dialogue. The numbers indicate where a sentence has been missed out. Decide where to put the following sentences. You can listen to the dialogue again to check your answers.

a) Why don't we all go home? ☐

b) I love you now. ☐

c) I've one more question to ask Mr Gatsby. 1

d) It's the truth. ☐

e) Why should I? ☐

f) She's never loved you. ☐

g) And I love Daisy too. ☐

h) Tell him you never loved him. ☐

Daisy Open the whisky, Tom, and I'll make everyone a drink.

Tom Wait a minute. (1)

Gatsby Go on.

Tom What kind of trouble are you trying to make between me and my wife?

Daisy Stop it, please, Tom.

Tom (2) Have I got to watch a nobody from nowhere make love to my wife and say nothing?

Gatsby Now, listen. I've got something to tell you, old sport.

Daisy Oh, please don't say anything. (3) It's too hot to argue.

Tom I want Mr Gatsby to give me an answer to my question.

Gatsby Your wife doesn't love you. (4) She loves me.

Tom You're crazy!

Gatsby (5) We've loved each other for five years, old sport, and you didn't know!

Tom I tell you you're crazy. Daisy loved me when she married me and she loves me now. (6) I always have. She knows that.

Gatsby Tell him the truth. (7)

Daisy I never loved him. Oh, you want too much, Jay! (8) Isn't that enough? I did love Tom once, but I loved you, too.

Gatsby You loved me, too …

Vocabulary

1 Read what these people say about themselves and decide which pairs would make good couples.

A

I guess the partner of my dreams would be an idealist like me – someone who is **loyal** and committed to the relationship, someone who is as over the moon about me as I am about them ... a true Romeo.

B

When my last relationship ended, I couldn't believe that someone could be so **two-faced**. For me, the most important qualities are sincerity and modesty. I don't care how **handsome** a guy is – that sort of guy is usually completely self-centred. I like the soft, **sensitive** type.

C

People say I can be fun to be with, I like chatting with friends and making jokes, and my perfect night out would be an evening of midnight skiing, followed by champagne in a moonlit restaurant with someone who doesn't get **stressed out** about saying how they feel.

D

I can be a bit over-sensitive at times, I get jealous really easily, and I find it easiest to talk to people who are **shy** like me. I get fed up with those bossy, **big-headed** types who think they're wonderful. Love isn't about status!

E

I'm not really looking for a long-term relationship. I want to have a good time on a date – I don't want to get engaged or anything. I can't see myself as the bride at a white wedding. I can't stand **narrow-minded** types – I prefer the easy-going sort.

F

I just like going out clubbing, having fun and stuff like that, and my relationships tend to be impulsive – you know, I meet someone who is really gorgeous-looking, and it starts like that.

G

For me, the most important thing in a partner is someone who shares my interests. I'm quite sporty and like dynamic, out-going types – I get on with really witty people who make me laugh, the **talkative** sort.

H

I suppose I prefer someone who is **old-fashioned** and romantic. I've always believed in love at first sight – I'm attracted to the reliable and faithful types, someone who would be completely devoted to me.

2 Find the words, in **bold** in Exercise 1, that are the opposites of the words below.

	opposite
broad-minded	_____
modern	_____
modest	_____
out-going	_____
quiet	_____
relaxed	_____
sincere	_____
thick-skinned	_____
ugly	_____
unfaithful	_____

3 Complete the sentences by matching the phrases from box A and box B.

A

a) Calm down and don't take
b) He's one of those people who has to be
c) I really feel that you should put
d) If you happen to change
e) It's very difficult to get
f) It's very important to take
g) She can make people feel
h) You should really try to learn

B

1 advantage of all the opportunities you get.
2 at ease, just by smiling at them.
3 close to people who are very private.
4 from your mistakes.
5 in control of everything and everyone.
6 things so seriously all the time.
7 your energy into something more useful.
8 your mind, will you let me know?

4 Which of the adjectives on this page could you use to describe the following people?

• yourself

_____

• a member of your family

_____

• someone in your class

_____

• a politician in your country

_____

Writing

Read the letter and answer the questions below.

1 Dear Vince,

2 I have been meaning to write to you for ages, and I'm sorry I didn't telephone you before I went back to Japan. I'm sorry I didn't get the chance to talk to you before I left, but everything happened very suddenly. I hope that you are well and that everything is going well with your job. How's it going with your studies? How is everyone at the college?

3 When I was in England, I really missed my friends back in Japan, so I was happy to get back here, to see everyone again and catch up with the news. Do you remember Masako? We often talk about you, and she sends her love. I have had letters from some of our friends in England. Do you still see them?

4 I've been looking for a job and I've written about thirty letters of application, but so far I haven't had any replies. Then, two days ago my father said that a friend of his was looking for someone who speaks English to work for two months as a receptionist in his company's office in London. Yesterday, I went for the interview and I got the job, so in three weeks I'll be back in England!

5 Do you still have the same phone number? I'll give you a ring when I arrive - perhaps we could meet up and go out for a meal or something like that? It would be great to see you again.

6 Love
   Chiyo

7 P.S. I've still got your umbrella!

---

1 Match the headings below to the parts of the letter.

a) the closing phrase [6]

b) news about mutual friends [ ]

c) introduction and apologies for not writing earlier [ ]

d) the opening phrase [ ]

e) news about the present and future plans [ ]

f) the main reason for writing [ ]

g) anything the writer forgot to mention earlier (postscript) [ ]

2 Match these beginnings of sentences to their endings.

a) Give me   1 your work?
b) I hope you're   2 best wishes.
c) I'm sorry I   3 hear from you again.
d) It was great to   4 to see you next week.
e) It would be great to   5 getting on well with your job.
f) How's it going with   6 meet up soon.
g) X sends his/her   7 a call.
h) I can't wait   8 didn't write sooner.

3 Imagine that you are Vincent and write a reply to Chiyo. In your letter, you may want to include some of the following points:

• thanks for her letter
• news about the past / mutual friends
• news about what you are doing now
• looking forward to seeing Chiyo

4 Adrenalin

Song lyrics

thrill /θrɪl/ **thrills, thrilling, thrilled**

1 If something gives you **a thrill**, it gives you a sudden feeling of great excitement, pleasure, or fear. *I can remember the thrill of not knowing what I would get on Christmas morning... It's a great thrill for a cricket-lover like me to play at the home of cricket. ...the realization that new adventures, new thrills, and new worlds lie ahead.*

◇◇◇◇◇
N-COUNT: usu sing, oft N of n/-ing

2 If something **thrills** you, or if you **thrill** at it, it gives you a feeling of great pleasure and excitement. *The electric atmosphere both terrified and thrilled him... The children will thrill at all their favourite characters.*

V-ERG
V n
V at/to n

kick /kɪk/ **kicks, kicking, kicked**

6 If something gives you **a kick**, it makes you feel very excited or very happy for a short period of time; an informal use. *I got a kick out of seeing my name in print.*

N-SING: a N

Translate these lines from a famous song by Cole Porter.

I get no kick from champagne
Mere alcohol doesn't thrill me at all
So tell me why should it be true
That I get a kick out of you?

Grammar

1 Match the sentences to the timelines below.

	Action 1	Action 2
a)	The exam finished	when I was doing the last exercise.
b)	I put down my pen	when the teacher said 'Stop'.
c)	I was thinking about something else	when he was explaining the exercise.
d)	I was feeling nervous	when the exam began.

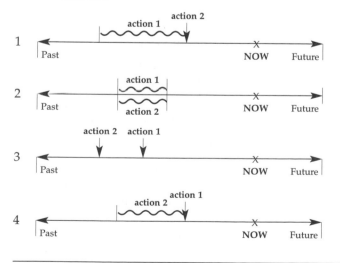

2 Put the verbs into the past simple or the past continuous.

a) Mike _____ a newspaper when he _____ an advert for skydiving. (read/see)

b) He _____ the skydiving centre and immediately _____ a jump. (phone/book)

c) He _____ his training a week later. (begin)

d) In the plane, the others _____ jokes, but Mike _____ really nervous. (make/feel)

e) It _____ the end of a beautiful day and the sun _____ down. (be/go)

f) The trainer _____ the door and Mike _____ out of the plane. (open/jump)

g) While he _____ , he _____ an incredible rush of adrenalin. (fall/feel)

h) After that, he _____ about skydiving all the time, even when he _____ . (think/work)

3 Quickly read the short paragraphs below and match them to the pictures on the next page.

The BASE jumper

a) One day, Leo was walking home after work. The sun was shining and he was feeling happy. Suddenly, he was seeing a group of people who were looking up at the top of a building. Some of them were pointing and some were holding cameras.

b) Leo was looking up, too. He was seeing a woman who was standing on the roof of the building. He was shouting 'Don't jump!'

c) Two helicopters were flying overhead. Quickly, the woman was waving at the helicopters and was jumping.

d) On the ground, two paramedics were standing by an ambulance. They were waiting for the jumper to land. Other people were still pointing and taking photos. Then, the parachute was opening.

4 Now read the story in Exercise 1 again. Some of the verbs need to be changed from the past continuous to the past simple. Change...

... 1 verb in paragraph a).

... 3 verbs in paragraph b).

... 2 verbs in paragraph c).

... 1 verb in paragraph d).

5 Circle the best tense in the sentences below.

Example

Two days ago, *I have seen* / (*saw*) a large group of people in the street.

a) They *have looked* / *were looking* very worried.

b) A woman *has been* / *was* on the roof of a tall building.

c) Everybody *has thought* / *thought* she was going to kill herself.

d) The newspapers say there *have been* / *were* a lot of suicides recently in the city.

e) After a few minutes, two helicopters *have arrived* / *arrived*.

f) When she saw the helicopters, the woman *jumped* / *was jumping*.

g) We could see that the woman *has smiled* / *was smiling*.

h) Everyone *has cheered* / *cheered* when she landed safely.

i) Since then, I *have thought* / *thought* about becoming a BASE jumper myself.

6 Read this interview with a BASE jumper and put the verbs in brackets into the correct tense: past simple, past continuous or present perfect.

Reporter: How long (a) _____ (you/be) a BASE jumper?

Jumper: About three years now. I (b) _____ (start) when I (c) _____ (study) at university.

Reporter: Why? It seems a crazy thing to do! What (d) _____ (give) you the idea?

Jumper: Well, I (e) _____ (always/enjoy) dangerous sports, and a friend (f) _____ (say) he would give me £100 if I did the jump.

Reporter: How many jumps (g) _____ (you/do)?

Jumper: About thirty so far – and I (h) _____ (never/have) an accident, thank God.

Reporter: (i) _____ (you/ever/think) about finding a safer hobby?

Jumper: Yes! I'm getting married later this year and I (j) _____ (promise) my partner that I will stop then.

7 Complete the following sentences by making a comparative or superlative form of the adjective.

a) What's _____
thing you've ever done? (exciting)

b) Scuba diving in the Bahamas was one of
_____ experiences
in my life. (enjoyable)

c) It was much _____
than I had imagined. (easy)

d) I think the Red Sea is _____
for scuba diving than the Bahamas. (good)

e) The Bahamas are a lot _____
and they are _____ .
(far, expensive)

f) But the hotels near the Red Sea are
_____ than those
in the Bahamas. (bad)

g) The coral is probably _____
_____ sight in the
world. (beautiful)

h) It was _____
holiday of my life. (good)

Vocabulary

1 Look at the word spiral and find 7 words connected with sport, 5 words connected with the body and 3 names of animals.

Sport

_____

_____

_____

The body

_____

_____

Animals

_____

2 You can combine adverbs with adjectives to make things stronger. Which adjectives can be combined with the adverbs in box A, and which with the adverbs in box B?

A

| absolutely
utterly |

B

| extremely
very |

amazing
brilliant
enjoyable
exciting
fantastic
interesting
incredible
lucky
nervous

3 Match the colloquial expressions to the meanings below.

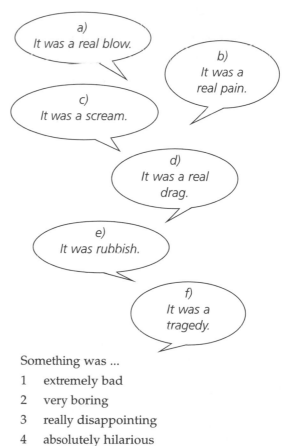

a) It was a real blow.

b) It was a real pain.

c) It was a scream.

d) It was a real drag.

e) It was rubbish.

f) It was a tragedy.

Something was ...

1 extremely bad
2 very boring
3 really disappointing
4 absolutely hilarious
5 very irritating
6 extremely sad

Listening

1 📼 Cover the tapescript and listen to four people talking about the most exciting holidays they have ever had. Match the speakers to the pictures. (If you don't have the recording, read the tapescript.)

a)

b)

c)

d)

2 📼 Listen again and decide if the following sentences are true (T) or false (F).

a) During the Canadian holiday they went flying every day. ☐

b) During the Canadian holiday, one plane crashed. ☐

c) During the swimming trip, they had to use special equipment. ☐

d) During the swimming trip they were attacked by sharks. ☐

e) The submarine trip lasted a week. ☐

f) The submarine trip was dark and it was hard to see. ☐

g) The Russian jet trip was painful. ☐

h) The Russian jet trip was filmed for the TV. ☐

3 📼 All of these expressions are used to describe experiences that are really good. Listen to how these words are said and practise them. You need to make your voice high!

Amazing!	Great!
Brilliant!	Incredible!
Fantastic!	Out of this world!
Wow!	

---

1 The most exciting thing I've ever done was when I spent a week in Canada. What we did was ... every afternoon we went up in a Harvard jet and you fly around looking for other jets. When you see one, you try to get it in your sights, you pull the trigger and fire – it's a kind of laser. If you manage to hit another plane, you hear this noise and you can see smoke. It was great, brilliant fun, but I could never afford to do it again. I'll never forget it – it was absolutely fantastic!

2 I was on holiday once in the Bahamas and I saw an advertisement for an excursion – 'Swim with the sharks' it said. I didn't really believe it, but I thought it was an incredible idea. Anyway, two days later I found myself on a boat with a group of other people. We put on scuba diving gear and a special kind of protection thing for the arms and then jumped in. The sharks arrived and there we were swimming with the sharks, playing with them – they came right up and touched us. To begin with I thought I would die, but then it was so peaceful, so beautiful – a totally amazing experience! Brilliant!

3 A few years ago, me and a friend of mine spent a week in the Canadian Arctic. One day we were taken out in a small submarine which took us under the ice. Just being under the water is strange enough. It was really dark, but we had big lights which lit everything up – weird fish, and one time something that looked like a shark, but I don't think it was. Then we came to this wreck – an old ship that had gone down over a hundred years ago. It was scary, but at the same time I thought, wow, this is just like too much.

4 Last summer I was in Russia and I was taken to an airbase just outside Moscow. There were two of us and this Russian guy and we got in a MiG-25. Take off was more like blast off, this thing was going at Mach 2, that's nearly fifteen hundred kilometres an hour, and it really hurts, it's hard to breathe and your head hurts, but then you look out of the window, and there it is, Planet Earth, just like in some film on the TV or something, and you think, God, that's just, just out-of-this-world.

Writing

1 Read these notes that a reporter made during an interview with a famous explorer. Then write the article about Wilfred Thesiger for the newspaper.

2 Before you write ...

- Check in a dictionary any words that you do not know.

- Look carefully at all the verbs in the notes. You will need to use the past simple and the present perfect. You may also need to use the present tense.

- Think about where you will need to put articles (*a, an, the*). Remember that you do not usually need an article when you are talking about a country, but geographical features like rivers and deserts need *the*, for example *The Pyrenees*.

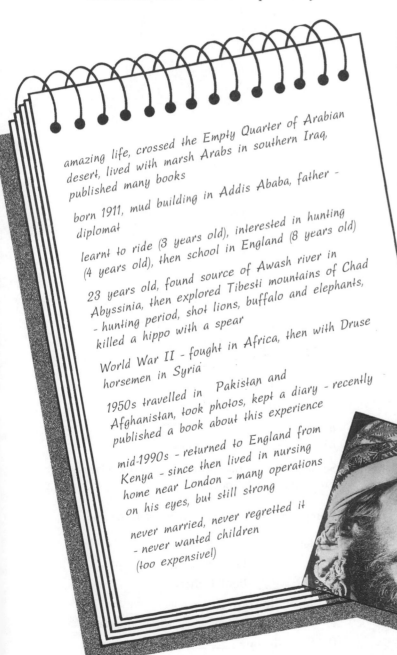

amazing life, crossed the Empty Quarter of Arabian desert, lived with marsh Arabs in southern Iraq, published many books

born 1911, mud building in Addis Ababa, father - diplomat

learnt to ride (3 years old), interested in hunting (4 years old), then school in England (8 years old)

23 years old, found source of Awash river in Abyssinia, then explored Tibesti mountains of Chad - hunting period, shot lions, buffalo and elephants, killed a hippo with a spear

World War II - fought in Africa, then with Druse horsemen in Syria

1950s travelled in Pakistan and Afghanistan, took photos, kept a diary - recently published a book about this experience

mid-1990s - returned to England from Kenya - since then lived in nursing home near London - many operations on his eyes, but still strong

never married, never regretted it - never wanted children (too expensive!)

Pronunciation

1 Look at the auxiliary verbs (*was, were, has, have*) in the following dialogues. In each dialogue, decide which verb is pronounced in the strong form and which is weak.

1 A: I was thinking of going skydiving.
　 B: Were you?!
2 A: We were beginning to feel nervous.
　 B: I wasn't!
3 A: She has never been hurt in a fight.
　 B: Well, I have!
4 A: Have you ridden a horse?
　 B: No, but my wife has.

	strong	*weak*
was	/wɒz/	/wəz/
were	/wɜː/	/wə/
has	/hæz/	/həz/
have	/hæv/	/həv/

Listen to the recording to check your answers and practise saying the sentences.

5 *Kids*

Kids' jokes

Can you get these jokes? Use a dictionary if you need to.

Grammar

1 Complete these sentences with a word from the box.

> that   when   where   which   who   whom   whose

I want...

a) a sister _____ doesn't pull my hair!

b) a house _____ has a garden!

c) a dog _____ back I could ride on!

d) a school _____ I like!

e) a teacher _____ I can understand!

f) more time _____ I can play!

g) toys _____ I don't have to share!

h) a place _____ I can hide!

Some of these sentences do not need a relative pronoun. Which ones?

2 Complete these sentences with *whose* or *who's*.

a) Find out _____ there.

b) _____ taken my calendar?

c) _____ book is that?

d) I want to know _____ yacht that is.

e) He's the boy _____ top of the class.

f) She's the one _____ pen I borrowed.

3 Rearrange the words in the definitions below.

Example
it place rains rarely where
It's a *place where it rarely rains.*

a) It's a _____
_____

decides guilty if is lawyer not or someone who

b) It's a _____
_____

fall the time start leaves when to

c) It's a _____
_____

after animals doctor kind looks of that

d) It's an _____
_____

animal in lived prehistoric that times

e) It's a _____
_____

finish get qualification that university when you you

f) It's a _____
_____

at is person studying university who

g) It's a _____
_____

baseball for hat kind of that wear you

4 In two of the sentences in Exercise 3, you can omit the relative pronoun. Which ones?

5 Can you find words from this unit which match the definitions you wrote in Exercise 3?

Example
It's a place where it rarely rains.
desert

a) _____
b) _____
c) _____
d) _____
e) _____
f) _____
g) _____

6 Join the pairs of sentences by making relative clauses.

Example
My dad is a nice man. He gives me lots of presents.
My dad is a nice man who gives me lots of presents.

a) Dad lives with a new girlfriend. I don't like her.
_____
_____

b) She has a daughter. I can't remember her name.
_____
_____

c) They have a house by the sea. I went there on holiday last year.
_____
_____

d) My mum and I live in a small flat. It doesn't have a garden.
_____
_____

e) Mum has a job. She really loves it.
_____
_____

f) She works in the morning. I am at school then.
_____
_____

g) I have a friend. Her mother works at the zoo.
_____
_____

h) This is a picture of my dad. I drew it.
_____
_____

7 Rewrite the following sentences using *used to*. Two of the sentences cannot be rewritten with *used to*. Leave them as they are.

a) I was always in trouble when I was a child.

_____

b) I arrived at school late every day.

_____

c) I was never any good at my studies.

_____

d) During break times, my friends and I smoked cigarettes behind the school.

_____

_____

e) One day, we were caught smoking.

_____

f) We were very rude to the teachers.

_____

g) All the teachers hated us.

_____

h) I had very long hair and wore one earring.

_____

i) I thought that school was a waste of time.

_____

j) Eventually, I was asked to leave the school.

_____

In two of the sentences above, you can change *used to* to *would*. Change these two sentences.

_____

_____

Vocabulary

1 The following are all words you have met in the first units of this book. Can you name them?

a) an animal that looks like a crocodile
   A _ _ _ _ _ _ _ R

b) a sort of large fish which can attack humans
   S _ _ _ K

c) a child who is learning to walk
   T _ _ _ _ _ R

d) the most senior teacher in a university
   P _ _ _ _ _ _ _ R

e) what you do when you are cold S _ _ _ _ R

f) the season when leaves fall A _ _ _ _ N

g) the people who watch a film or a play
   A _ _ _ _ _ _ E

h) a thief who steals from houses B _ _ _ _ _ R

i) the written words that are used to translate a film on screen   S _ _ _ _ _ _ _ S

j) an animal with a hard shell that lives in the sea T _ _ _ _ E

2 Complete these sentences with a preposition from the box.

across	at	down	for	in	off	on
to						

a) A mum is a person who cares _____ you.

b) He was staring _____ me in a peculiar way.

c) I took a qualification _____ engineering.

d) Paintings are displayed _____ the public in art galleries.

e) The girls were _____ their way home.

f) He went speeding _____ the hill.

g) I walked home _____ the fields.

h) Don't take your hands _____ the steering wheel.

3 Match the words in the box to the numbers in the sentences below.

a)	ambition *1*	i)	jungle
b)	deaf	j)	naughty
c)	degree	k)	pilot *2*
d)	desert	l)	punish
e)	fabulous	m)	shark
f)	float	n)	thumb
g)	hell	o)	undergraduate
h)	iceberg	p)	yell

Some children have this (1) to become this (2).

Some people believe that this (3) is hotter than this (4).

The world of business is sometimes called this (5) and it's full of these (6).

You are one of these (7) until you get one of these (8).

One of these (9) can do this (10).

You may do this (11) if a child is this (12).

You may have to do this (13) if someone is a little this (14).

You may put this (15) up if you think something is this (16).

Listening and reading

John Carr, a teacher who works in a London secondary school, was asked about his worst teaching experience.

1 📼 Cover the tapescript and listen to the teacher's story and put these events in the order in which they happened. (If you don't have the recording, read the story.)

a) A child started crying. ☐

b) The teacher went to look for the children. ☐

c) The headmaster spoke to the teacher. ☐

d) A child left the room. ☐

e) The teacher realised the students had tricked him. ☐

f) The students began a test. ☐

g) The teacher returned to the classroom. ☐

h) A child's mother died. ☐1

i) The child's friend went to find her. ☐

2 Read the story and find expressions which mean the same as the following:

a) had no idea *(paragraph 1)*

b) make your life difficult *(paragraph 1)*

c) she still hadn't come back *(paragraph 4)*

d) the only thing to do was *(paragraph 4)*

e) very well-behaved *(paragraph 5)*

3 Find three places in the first paragraph where you can add *that*. An example has been done for you.

              that

I think that the worst experience ʌ I have ever had was in my first year of teaching, and the kids knew that I didn't have a clue how to control them. I was giving the students a French test, a subject most of them hate. I had this class of third years – they're the worst, children who do anything they can to give you a hard time, spotty adolescents. It's the age-range I hate most.

There was a girl whose mother had just died and she used to just sit there and stare at me as if it was my fault. And there was another who used to sit next to her who was probably the biggest trouble-maker in the school.

Anyway, one day, the students were doing this test – it was about the subjunctive, which we had just done in class – when this girl started crying. She put up her hand and asked if she could go to the toilet. I knew that she was probably thinking about her mother, so I said yes. I mean, what else could I do? She left the room and ten minutes later she still hadn't come back. I was wondering what to do next when the other girl put her hand up and asked if she could go and look for her friend. I couldn't go myself because the students would all cheat, so I said yes, and she left the room, too.

Ten minutes later there was still no sign of her. I thought there was nothing for it but to go and find them both myself. I was just coming out of the girls' loo – they weren't there – when the headmaster called me from the other end of the corridor. 'Mr Carr!' he shouted. 'Is there any particular reason why your class are all talking to each other in the middle of an exam? I suggest you get back there and supervise them. Immediately!'

I ran back to my classroom and there were the two girls, sitting quietly, as good as gold. The rest of the class were also quiet, busily getting on with their test. It was only when I marked the test that I realised I had been tricked. The whole class scored more than 80% – the first and last time that ever happened!

Writing

1 Read the advertisement and the letter that has been written in reply. Put the sentences from the letter in the correct order.

Deptford School of English

✓ Open all year
✓ Classes for all levels
✓ Prepare for Cambridge PET, FCE and CAE examinations
✓ Excellent quality accommodation

Deptford is a lively suburb of London near to the River Thames, Greenwich and the Millennium Dome

ENROL NOW!

For a brochure or further details, please contact Deptford School of English, 13 Hague Square, London SE27 4ZY

Workstay Programme

We'll find you a job in London!
➤ 100s of jobs (tour guides, home helps, bar work, etc)
➤ Guaranteed minimum wage ◄——— How much?
➤ Cheap accommodation in ◄——— How much?
   London suburbs ◄——— Accommodation near Deptford?
➤ Flexible start dates
➤ Cheap travel and work insurance

Send a cheque for only £20 to ◄——— Pay by credit card?
register now!
Workstay Programme,
Unit 27, The Arches, London
SE27D 0SH

---

a) I look forward to hearing from you. ☐

b) Dear Sir / Madam, ☐1

c) and I would be grateful if you could send me a brochure. ☐

d) I would also like more information about the range of accommodation that you offer. ☐

e) If so, please send me further details. ☐

f) I am interested in following an English language course in the summer of next year ☐

g) yours faithfully, ☐

h) I would like to know if it is possible to take a Cambridge examination at the end of the summer. ☐

i) I am writing in response to your advertisement in 'Travel Times'. ☐

2 You want to get a job in London next summer. Write a reply to the advertisement at the top of the column opposite. Use the letter above and the notes to help you.

Pronunciation

1 🔊 Listen to *The Little Red Rap*.

> Just on the edge
> of a deep, dark wood
> lived a girl called
> Little Red Riding Hood.
> Her grandmother lived
> not far away,
> so Red went to pay her
> a visit one day…
>
> And the Big Bad Wolf,
> who knew her plan
> he turned his nose
> and ran and ran.
> He ran till he came
> to her grandmother's door.
>
> Then he locked her up
> with a great big roar.
> He took her place
> in her nice warm bed,
> and he waited there
> for Little Miss Red.

Now listen again and repeat each line, copying the speed and rhythm.

News

Headlines

Can you match these headlines of famous events, all taken from newspapers at the time, to their dates?

1950 1959 1961 1963 1973 1975

Batista Flees From Country: Havana Casinos, Shops Looted

PINOCHET TAKES POWER IN COUP D'ETAT

SPANISH MONARCHY RESTORED

Kennedy Assassinated: Is Shot Down in Car by a Hidden Sniper

North Korea Invades South Korea

Russia Fires First Astronaut Into Space

Which headlines include a passive structure?

Grammar

1 Complete the table with past participles.

acquit		hide	
ban		hurt	
bring		keep	
cancel		shoot	
choose		spy	
drink		throw	

2 Complete the sentences with passive verbs. You will need to use the present simple, past simple or present perfect.

a) The rock star, Sonia Thorne, _____ _____ at Heathrow Airport last night. (arrest)

b) She _____ by customs officers after arriving on a flight from Amsterdam. (stop)

c) Almost two kilos of cocaine _____ _____ in her luggage. (find)

d) This is the second time that Ms Thorne _____ _____ on drugs charges. (arrest)

e) However, she _____ _____ (never/convict).

f) Ms Thorne _____ overnight in police cells. (keep)

g) Because of the arrest, her concert at Wembley Arena _____ . (cancel)

h) It _____ that she will appear in court later today. (believe)

3 Rewrite these sentences using a passive verb.

Example
The paparazzi pursued the car for 10 kilometres.
The car was pursued for 10 kilometres.

a) People stare at her when she walks down the street.
She _____ _____

b) The newspaper will pay her $50,000 compensation for the embarrassing photos.
She _____

_____

c) Thieves stole an enormous sum of money from a Hollywood celebrity last night.
Last night, an enormous sum of money_____

_____

d) Police have charged the footballer, Robert Flower, with assault.
The footballer, Robert Flower, _____

_____

e) The editor sacked the journalist for inventing the story.
The journalist _____

f) A judge has acquitted two photographers of invasion of privacy.
Two photographers _____
_____

g) Security guards protect his house from spying paparazzi.
His house _____
_____

h) They will splash her photo all over the front pages.
Her photo _____
_____

4 Change one verb in each of the following news stories. Some need to be changed from active to passive, and some from passive to active.

Example

> Donald Thomas ~~was~~ escaped from prison in Rhode Island, US, after serving 89 days of a 90-day sentence. He was captured and sentenced to an extra six months.

> a)
> Philip Johnson, 32, from Prestonburg, Kentucky, shot himself in the chest because he wanted to see if it would hurt. He was discovered that it does.

> b)
> Bank robber John Perkins, 37, arrested at Los Angeles airport. When he was asked if he had anything to declare, he joked 'Only a bomb!' Customs men searched his bag and found the stolen money.

> c)
> André Gurmon, from Lyons, France, was put an advert in the newspaper saying: 'Ladies – write to me if you are bored with the man in your life.' He received a reply from his wife.

> d)
> Francesco Rivera, 26, from Pisa in Italy, was on his way to a fancy-dress party and was dressed as a gorilla. He shot with tranquiliser darts by local zoo keepers.

> e)
> Circus girl Jacquelyn LaBow, 22, jailed for six days in Nice for riding naked on an elephant on a busy road.

> f)
> Harrison Ford has false teeth. Ford was made the confession after an American magazine voted him the sexiest man alive.

5 Complete the story with words from the box.

attacked	be	been	broke	broken
gave	given	had	keep	kept
really	saw	seen	taken	was

Police probe Duffy scandal

Top Hollywood film star, Tom Duffy, cannot (a) _____ out of the news and it is usually for all the wrong reasons.

His latest troubles started a few months ago when a compromising photograph of Anna, Duffy's wife, (b) _____ published in a Hollywood magazine. She was (c) _____ in a Los Angeles nightclub, The Lounge Lizard, with her arm around Bruce Cashman, Tom's co-star in his latest film, *Dirty Business*. 'Since then,' a friend of the couple reported, 'they have (d) _____ many fights. Only last week, he (e) _____ her a black eye.'

Then, late last night, Anna called the police and complained that Duffy had (f) _____ her again. 'Mrs Duffy said that she was thrown down the stairs, and that Mr Duffy then (g) _____ her nose when he hit her with the handle of his gun,' said an LAPD spokesperson. 'Mr Duffy was (h) _____ to Santa Monica police station and a statement will be (i) _____ to the press later today.'

Reporters who (j) _____ Mr Duffy at the station said that he denied the incident. 'Of course, her nose isn't (k) _____,' he told them, 'I hardly touched her. She (l) _____ made me angry, but I wouldn't hurt her.'

Mrs Duffy has been (m) _____ in hospital so that some more X-ray photos of her nose can (n) _____ taken. Sources at the hospital report that she has already (o) _____ visited by Mr Cashman.

Vocabulary

1 Join the beginnings and ends of these sentences by using a preposition from the box in the middle. An example has been done for you.

a) The demonstrators were charged

b) The government took pity

c) The machine is dangerously

d) The police car chased them

e) The president is not available

f) The thieves were sentenced

g) The victims will receive $5000

| at |
| with |
| on |
| out of |
| for |
| to |
| in |

1) comment.

2) ten years in prison.

3) high speed.

4) compensation.

5) the victims of the drought.

6) disturbing the peace.

7) control.

Example
The demonstrators were charged with disturbing the peace.

a) _____

_____

b) _____

_____

c) _____

_____

d) _____

_____

e) _____

_____

f) _____

_____

2 Circle the correct word.

a) He is a *support/supporter/supportive* of Arsenal Football Club.

b) The match was abandoned because of an *invasion/invader/invasive* of the pitch.

c) They were found guilty of *murder/murderer/murderous*.

d) Have you read any of the company's *promotion/promoter/promotional* literature?

e) Parents are usually *protection/protector/protective* of their children.

f) The *judgement/judge/judgmental* did not allow the press to enter the court.

g) I thought their behaviour was unusually *aggression/aggressor/aggressive*.

h) The *destruction/destroyer/destructive* of the rain forest is very worrying.

3 Replace one word in each of the following sentences with a word or expression from the box.

| chased | cry | married | help | leave |
| split up | | | | |

a) He started to sob when he heard the bad news.

b) He surprised his colleagues when he wed the managing director.

c) She decided to quit her job when a new boss arrived.

d) The refugees will receive aid from some charities.

e) She was pursued by a pack of photographers.

f) They decided to separate after being together for ten years.

Pronunciation

1 Circle the word which has a different vowel sound from the other words.

a) shark   past   laugh   ball   calm
b) caught all   talked door   hard
c) wrong   half   block   yacht   want
d) hill   lived   field   wish   list
e) student mum   young   judge   month

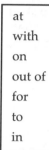 Listen and check your answers.

Listening and reading

A radio phone-in programme is discussing the following questions:
Reporting of celebrity scandals in the press: should it be banned? Are scandals in the private lives of famous people any of our business?

1 ⬛ Cover the tapescript and listen to eight people giving their opinions. Do they think that these stories and photos should (A) be allowed, or (B) be banned?

Speaker	A or B ?
Anna	_____
Rod	_____
Mike	_____
Wendy	_____
Steve	_____
Andy	_____
Diane	_____
Alice	_____

2 Read what the people said and look at the verbs that are *in italics*. Then use those verbs, in the correct form, in the definitions below.

a) If you _____ something, you agree with it.

b) If you _____ something, you manage or survive quite well without it.

c) If you _____ doing something, you stop doing it.

d) If you _____ something, you invent it.

e) If you _____ someone, you respect or admire them.

f) If something _____ , it stops working.

g) If you _____ about something, you learn about it.

h) If you _____ doing something, you continue to do it and do not stop.

i) If you _____ something, you want it to happen because you think you will like it.

Anna I don't think that it's got anything to do with us, it's none of our business. If people want to do what they want, I don't care who they are, they should be allowed to. I think we can *do without* this kind of thing in the papers.

Rod I think that the problem is that half of the stuff they print is just complete rubbish. They'll print anything to make a bit of money, and I think that half the time they just *make it up*. I don't think they should be allowed to print a load of lies.

Mike A lot of people, especially young people, *look up to* pop stars and film stars and people like that, so my feeling is that it's important we know what they're up to. These people are role models for our children, so it's right if we know what they are really like.

Wendy I really like *finding out* about who's going out with who, who's getting married and that kind of thing. I get 'Hello' every week and it gives you all the latest news and I really *look forward to* it. What's wrong with that?

Steve I can't see how it is in the public's interest to know about the private life of a Hollywood film star or some princess or other. It may be that these people have immoral lives but it's even more immoral to write and read about it. I don't *go along with* this kind of thing at all.

Andy If people want to read information like this, then the newspapers will print it. I don't think you can blame the newspapers. If people *gave up* buying these papers, then you wouldn't get all these shock-horror stories. It's as simple as that.

Diane I think it's really important that the press has complete freedom. After all, if you start saying 'No, you can't print this, you can't print that', it won't be long before our whole democratic society *breaks down*. I don't want politicians deciding what I can read.

Alice Well, these film stars say they're not happy about it but they *keep on* giving interviews all the time, so I can't see how they can complain if sometimes the papers print stories about them that are maybe a bit embarrassing. That's just too bad for them!

Writing

1 Complete the sentences below with a word or expression from the box.

> *Contrasting ideas*
>
> - *although*
>
>   Although he fell over 200 metres, he only hurt his foot.
>
>   Although there was a drought, there was no shortage of water.
>
> - *despite*
>
>   Despite falling over 200 metres, he only hurt his foot.
>
>   Depite the drought, there was no shortage of water.
>
> - *however* or *nevertheless*
>
>   He fell over 200 metres. However/Nevertheless, he only hurt his foot.
>
>   There was a drought. However/Nevertheless, there was no shortage of water.

a) He kept on interrupting _____ he said that he would keep quiet.

b) I find these stories annoying. _____ , I continue to read them

c) The judge acquitted her _____ the evidence against her.

d) Cigarettes have been banned here. _____ , people still smoke.

e) _____ feeling very tired, she chased after the thieves.

f) _____ it was an unflattering picture of him, he quite liked it.

2 You are going to write an essay about invasion of privacy by the press.

- Use the essay plan below to help you.
- On a piece of paper, write your essay plan. Use the ideas in the 'Listening and reading' section to help you.
- Before you start, look at the language in the box below to help you.

> **Celebrity scandals in the press: should they be banned?**
>
> *Paragraph 1*
> Introduction: explain that some people think the reporting of celebrity scandals in the press should be banned. You may like to give an example of such a scandal.
>
> *Paragraph 2*
> Give your opinion and choose one or two reasons for this. Also give arguments against your reasons.
>
> *Paragraph 3*
> Choose one or two more reasons and also give arguments against.
>
> *Paragraph 4*
> Conclusion: give your opinion again.

> In my opinion, it is true to say …
> Personally, I believe / don't believe that …
>
> Having said that, it is important to remember that …
> At the same time, I feel that …
> Although some people feel …
> Perhaps the most important point, however, is …
>
> What is more, …
> Another important consideration is that …
> One of the main arguments against … is …
>
> All things considered, it is fair to say that …
> In conclusion, / On balance, I would say that …

7 Party

Party, party

Can you do this quiz?

1   Which of these is *not* a kind of party where
    people enjoy themselves?
    a) garden   b) hen   c) stag   d) third .

2   Which of these *is* a kind of party where people
    enjoy themselves?
    a) guilty   b) search   c) tea   d) working

3   Which of these is *not* a kind of party?
    a) function   b) host   c) rave   d) reception

4   Which of these verbs *can't* you use to complete
    the following sentence?
    I _____ the party.
    a) assisted   b) gatecrashed   c) held
    d) threw

5   Which of these is *not* a children's party game?
    a) Grandmother's footsteps   b) Musical chairs
    c) Pass the parcel   d) Trivial pursuit

6   Which of these is *not* an English political party?
    a) Conservative   b) Labour
    c) Liberal Democrat   d) Popular

Grammar

1 Find an appropriate response in box B for the
    sentences in box A.

A

> a) Do you fancy going to the cinema tonight?
>
> b) Have you got any plans for the summer?
>
> c) What are you doing next Tuesday evening?
>
> d) Do you think Roger would like to come?
>
> e) Are you going to see them off at the
>   airport?
>
> f) Have you seen the new Almodovar film
>   yet?
>
> g) Have you bought anything for his
>   birthday yet?
>
> h) How much longer are you going to wait
>   for him?
>
> i) Do you think you'll ever get that
>   promotion?

B

> 1 Hang on. I'll have a look in my diary.
>
> 2 Yes! I'm driving them there!
>
> 3 I don't know. I'm seeing the boss
>   tomorrow.
>
> 4 I'll give him another ten minutes, then I'll
>   give up.
>
> 5 I can't, I'm afraid. I'm having dinner at
>   my parents'.
>
> 6 No, I'm going to get him some CDs.
>
> 7 Unfortunately, yes. I'm going to stay here
>   and decorate the flat.
>
> 8 No, I'm going to see it some time next
>   week.
>
> 9 Have you got your mobile? I'll give him a
>   call.

2 There is one mistake in each of the following
    mini-dialogues. Make the correction.

1   A: Are you going to get married soon?
    B: Maybe. I'll to let you know when we've
        fixed the date.

2   A: Where you are going to find the money?
    B: The bank! I'm seeing the bank manager
        on Friday.

3   A: You will write to me often, won't you?
    B: Yes. I've decided that I'm going write a
        letter every morning.

4   A: OK, I'll give you a call tomorrow night.
    B: No, don't. I going to be out tomorrow.

5   A: Are you coming to the party?
    B: Yes, I'll being there.

6   A: Aren't you going help him with that?
    B: No, I think I'll let him do it on his own.

3 Put the verbs in brackets into the correct form.
    Use the present continuous, *going to* or *'ll* +
    infinitive. Sometimes more than one verb form is
    possible.

A: What are you looking so pleased about?

B: I've just got my tickets. I (a) _____
    (go) to London at the weekend.

A: What? Just for the weekend?

B: Yes, it's the Notting Hill Carnival. I
(b) _____ (leave) early on
Saturday morning at 6.30.

A: Where do you think (c) _____
(you/stay)? (d) _____
(you/look) for a hotel when you arrive?

B: I don't know. I haven't really thought about it
yet.

A: I tell you what. I (e) _____
(give) you Maite's number. She might have
room in her flat.

B: No, she (f) _____ (visit) her
parents this weekend. Do you know anyone
else in London?

A: My parents might know someone.
I (g) _____ (ask) them this
evening and I (h) _____ (let)
you know. Anyway, what is this carnival?

B: It's the biggest carnival in Europe – parades,
dancing, music and over a million people.
I (i) _____ (take) my camera,
and when I get back, I (j) _____
(show) you the pictures.

A: Oh, thanks! And I (k) _____
(tell) you all about my wonderful weekend.
I've got no money at all at the moment, so
I (l) _____ (watch) TV – all
weekend, probably.

4 Replace the words in italics with *it* or *them*.
Sometimes you will need to change the word
order of the sentence.

Example
I hope you're not going to light up *that cigar* in
here.
I hope you're not going to light it up in here.

a) I'm going to see off *some friends* at the station.

_____

_____

b) We'll get down to *business* as soon as possible.

_____

_____

c) We'll burn down *the palace* when the
revolution comes.

_____

_____

d) Are you looking forward to *the party*?

_____

_____

e) Do you think we'll run out of *cigarettes*?

_____

_____

f) He felt he'd let down *his parents* when he
failed his exams.

_____

_____

g) Let's put off *the party* until next week.

_____

_____

h) I hope I don't run into *those guys* again.

_____

_____

5 Complete the sentences below with a word from
the box.

could	do	doing	going	nothing
prefer	trying	would		

a) Frances, are you _____ anything at
the weekend?

b) I'd love to. What about _____ that
new place by the station?

c) I'm going there tonight actually. I'd
_____ somewhere different.

d) _____ special. Why?

e) OK. Let's _____ that, then.

f) OK. _____ you like to try the
Mexican in the main square?

g) Well, I wondered if you fancied
_____ out at the weekend.

h) Yes, great. We _____ meet for a
drink first and then go to the restaurant later.

6 The dialogue in Exercise 5 has been mixed up.
Put it into the correct order.

1 [*a*]
2 [ ]
3 [ ]
4 [ ]
5 [ ]
6 [ ]
7 [ ]
8 [ ]

Vocabulary

1 Complete the crossword.

1 He turned _____ two hours late.

2 Have you made any _____ for the future?

3 Are you ready _____ order yet?

4 Why did they go _____ on their promise?

5 (across) Fortunately, the bomb didn't _____ off.

5 (down) We should really _____ going.

6 I think you _____ that story up!

7 They were _____ off at the airport by all their friends.

8 He completely _____ us in when he said he was ill – everyone believed him!

9 It took her two weeks to get _____ the operation.

10 She _____ on really well with everyone.

11 He _____ off the idea when he realised how much it would cost.

12 The teacher made the grammar exercise _____ a game.

13 It's late. We must get down _____ some work.

14 She got out _____ the car and locked the door.

15 They put _____ their holiday until the autumn.

2 Match a word in box A with a word in box B to make logical combinations.

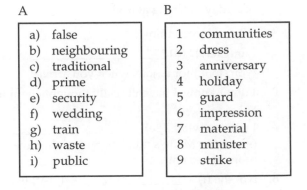

A

a)	false
b)	neighbouring
c)	traditional
d)	prime
e)	security
f)	wedding
g)	train
h)	waste
i)	public

B

1	communities
2	dress
3	anniversary
4	holiday
5	guard
6	impression
7	material
8	minister
9	strike

_____

_____

_____

_____

_____

_____

_____

_____

_____

3 Use the word at the end of each line to form a word which fits the gap.

a) I have absolutely no _____ of helping you. *intend*

b) He only goes to parties very _____ . *occasion*

c) His _____ at the party was scandalous – we won't invite him again. *behave*

d) The bomb was packed with nails and high _____ . *explode*

e) We'll need her full _____ before we do it. *agree*

f) She has an excellent _____ with her children. *relation*

g) The room was filled with _____ objects. *decorate*

h) Have you made all the _____ for the party? *prepare*

Reading

1

Every February on Shrove Tuesday, the people in Binche in Belgium put on huge ostrich feather hats and dress as Incas to commemorate the Spanish conquest of Peru. The celebration began in 1549 when Binche was under Spanish rule, but is still carried on today. The Gilles (dancers) parade through the town and throw oranges, which are said to symbolise the gold of the Incas, at passers-by. Other young men carry sticks and hit anyone who is not wearing a fancy hat or a red nose.

2

Every summer in Japan, people celebrate the Tanabata, the day when it is believed that Vega can cross the Milky Way to rediscover her lover. The night before, the sky is lit up with fireworks and on the day itself, people write their wishes on pieces of coloured paper, which they hang on bamboo branches. The next day, the messages are dropped in the river and float away.

3

On 2nd February in Arles-sur-Tech in the French Pyrenees, a man dresses up as a bear with a furry coat and mask, and is chased by villagers armed with guns and sticks. They catch him, tie him up, allow him to escape, and chase him again, throwing things at him. Eventually, they pretend to shoot him. Then everyone in the village dances around the dead bear of winter and welcomes the coming of spring.

4

In Mexico, 2 November is the Day of the Dead when, in the old Aztec religion, the dead return to life. Families go into the cemeteries, sit around the tombstones and offer food and tequila to the dead, before sitting down for a picnic, when they eat chocolate coffins and sugar skeletons.

5

The Battle of the Wine takes place each June in Haro, in northern Spain. Early in the morning, the people of the town go out to a church on a hill nearby. As soon as people leave the church, others attack them with wine. Soon, everyone is dancing to brass band music under a rain of wine and everyone's white T-shirts turn pink. When the ground is completely soaked in wine, people gather for a breakfast of snails and bread.

Extracts from The Guinness Book of Oddities
© 1995 Geoff Tibballs and Guinness World Records Ltd
Guinness is a Registered Trade Mark of Guinness World Records Ltd

1 Answers the questions by putting the numbers 1, 2, 3, 4 or 5 in the boxes.

a) In which festivals do people not throw things? ☐ ☐

b) In which festival do lots of people wear strange costumes? ☐

c) In which festival does someone dress up as an animal? ☐

d) In which festival is it a good idea to wear a hat? ☐

e) Which festival takes place in Asia? ☐

f) Which festival is based on old religious beliefs? ☐

g) Which festival lasts more than one day? ☐

h) Which festival happens latest in the year? ☐

2 Find the names for the things pictured on this page. You will find the words in the text.

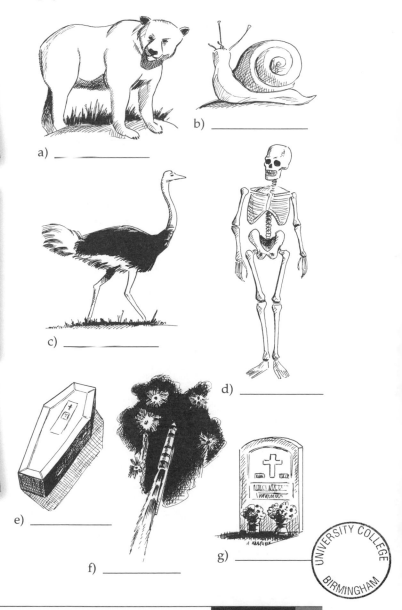

a) _____

b) _____

c) _____

d) _____

e) _____

f) _____

g) _____

Writing

1 Read these two letters which have been mixed up.

Dear David,

(1) I am just writing to say how much I enjoyed your party at the weekend. (2) I feel awful about it and I hope you'll forgive me. (3) There was a really good atmosphere and we all had a wonderful time.

(4) You must have spent ages getting everything ready. (5) The food was wonderful and the cocktails you prepared were out of this world. (6) It was a really good idea to have the music and the dancing in the garden, too. (7) What an embarrassment!

(8) Anyway, thanks again. (9) I promise that it won't happen again, although you probably won't invite me next time. (10) When I've had the film developed, I'll send you the best pictures.

Love
Helen

Dear David,

(1) I thought that I really should write to you to say how sorry I was about last weekend. (2) I didn't see you when I left, which is why I'm writing to thank you now. (3) I hate to think what the others must think of me!

(4) I know I shouldn't have been dancing on the table, but I was having such a good time. (5) I'm afraid I didn't realise that it wasn't strong enough for my weight. (6) I don't know what to say. (7) Brilliant!

(8) Anyway, please accept my apologies for being so stupid. (9) It was an evening I'll never forget. (10) I hope the enclosed cheque will cover the damage.

Best wishes,
Benita

2 In each letter, find three sentences which belong to the other letter.

_____

_____

_____

3 Look at the letters again and underline any expressions that are useful in letters of apology or thanks.

4 Decide if the following expressions are used in letters of apology or thanks. Write A (apology) or T (thanks) in the box.

a) I'd like to apologise for … ☐

b) Can you ever forgive me for …? ☐

c) You can't imagine how pleased I was to … ☐

d) I'll always remember … ☐

e) You must forgive me for … ☐

f) I'm awfully sorry about … ☐

g) I was so happy to … ☐

h) It was just what I … ☐

i) I wish I hadn't … ☐

j) I didn't mean to … ☐

k) It was really kind of you to … ☐

5 Now choose two situations and write a short letter for each.

- A person you don't know has sent you a parcel containing the purse/wallet that you lost a few days before.
- You have forgotten someone's birthday.
- You have just come back from visiting and staying with a friend in New York.
- You have lost or damaged something that you borrowed.

Review

Grammar

1 Complete the following story by putting one word in each space.

Four-year old Charlie Barnhead, (a) _____ lives with his parents in Buttsville, Arkansas, suffers from a strange disorder (b) _____ has the doctors puzzled. (c) _____ he was two years old, little Charlie (d) _____ seen dozens of doctors who (e) _____ been asked by his parents to find a cure for Charlie's problems. I was asked by my newspaper to get the story. During the interview with Charlie's parents, the boy (f) _____ lying quietly on the floor. After a few minutes, I realised that he was eating a new carpet that his parents had brought back from a recent holiday in Turkey. How (g) _____ does it cost them, I wondered. I asked them (h) _____ often he behaved like that. They said the problem (i) _____ not serious at first, but that (j) _____ the last few weeks it had been non-stop. Doctors in Arkansas can do nothing to help him, but the Barnheads (k) _____ saving up for a trip to Budapest (l) _____ there is a doctor who specialises in such problems. 'We're going (m) _____ do (n) _____ we can for little Charlie,' said his mother, 'but we don't know if we (o) _____ be able to save the money we need.'

2 Each of the following sentences has one word which should not be there. Cross it out.

a) Who did gave you that ice cream?

b) What is your teacher look like?

c) I have a massage from time to the time.

d) I haven't been going to a concert for ages.

e) They have lived there for six years between 1993 and 1999.

f) Glen has worked there since he has left college.

g) It was a very brilliant film: you should go and see it.

h) Have I ever been told you about the time I met Julia Roberts?

i) Sarah Flowers is the person you want to speak to her.

j) He got up, was accused me of staring at him and walked out.

k) The Pope is going to be visit Moscow.

l) This year's Oscar was being won by the latest Spielberg film.

m) Are you going doing anything interesting tonight?

n) Next time I will see him, I'll tell him what I think.

3 Use the word at the end of each line to form a word which fits the gap.

Example
I'm sorry – that's my final _____. *decide*
I'm sorry – that's my final *decision*.

a) I _____ go to the cinema at the weekend. *normal*

b) Have you ever _____ Mezcal? *drink*

c) I found his behaviour extremely _____. *annoy*

d) He hopes to go _____ round the States on his Harley. *travel*

e) It's a university which _____ in technical subjects. *special*

f) My personal _____ is very important to me. *private*

g) Did you get _____ to print those photos? *permit*

h) *Going to* is often used to express _____. *intend*

i) Many walkers are concerned about the _____ of country paths by mountain bikes. *destroy*

j) She was fined £100 as a _____ for speeding. *punish*

4 Rewrite the second sentence so that it has a similar meaning to the first sentence, beginning with the words given.

a) It's ages since I last went to the cinema.

I haven't _____

_____

b) She first met him when they were students.

She has _____

_____

c) It's her first bungee jump.

She has _____

_____

d) He can't find his keys.

He has _____

_____

e) It was a sunny day when they set off.

The sun _____

_____

f) The boy's parents were ill so he went to stay with his aunt.

The boy, whose _____

_____

_____

g) A friend of mine was arrested last week.

The police _____

_____

h) You are not allowed to take photographs here.

Photographs must _____

_____

i) I've arranged to see my parents at the weekend.

I am _____

_____

j) Salmon and a green salad for me.

I _____

_____

5 Find a response in box B to the conversational remarks in box A.

A

```
a) Any ideas for a leaving present for him?
b) Are you going to invite them to the
   party?
c) Do you still see your old school friends?
d) Did you know it was my birthday?
e) Have you heard about the train strike?
f) I think Helen would be a good person for
   the job.
g) I'll give you a call when I get back.
h) I'll pick you up at the station if you like.
i) Is her father feeling any better?
j) I've just failed my driving test again.
```

B

```
1  Her! You must be joking!
2  How about getting some CDs?
3  I suppose so, but I don't really want to.
4  Maybe third time lucky.
5  Now and again, but less and less.
6  OK. Have a good time!
7  Really? Many happy returns!
8  Thanks, but don't bother. I'll get a taxi.
9  To be honest, I forgot to ask.
10 Yes, what a nuisance!
```

Pronunciation

1 In these groups of words, one word has a different vowel sound. Which one?

a) host   post   cost   most

b) bomb   some   song   want

c) cool   cook   look   wood

d) gift   trip   third   risk

e) life   liked   lived   lines

f) reach   steal   street   meant

g) guest   spent   least   friend

Listen to the words and practise saying them.

2 Each of the words in the box contains a silent letter. Circle it.

```
bomb   castle   comb   folk
listen   talk   tomb   walk
whistle   wrap   written   wrong
```

Listen to the words and practise saying them.

Vocabulary

1 Circle the correct word.

a) Have you had the results yet of the exams you *passed/took* last week?

b) His driving is *terrible/terrific*: he shouldn't be allowed on the road.

c) It was so *bored/boring* that we went home early.

d) I've got to *avoid/ignore* fatty foods until I lose a bit of weight.

e) I was *robbed/stolen* on the way home from work last night.

f) She's going to work as an au pair for a year after the end of her *career/studies*.

g) We really enjoyed ourselves: it was great *fun/funny*.

h) We saw a film last night that was *absolutely/extremely* incredible.

i) When I get depressed, I wish people would *leave/let* me alone.

j) You shouldn't be so *sensible/sensitive*: it was only a joke!

2 Complete the sentences below with a word from the box.

did	got	had	made	put	spent
took	went				

a) How much time have you _____ doing this exercise?

b) I _____ a lot of running when I was younger, but then I gave it up.

c) I _____ a lot in common with my friends at school.

d) It really is time that you _____ a decision about your future.

e) The view at the top of the mountain really _____ my breath away.

f) They _____ their jobs at risk by being rude to the boss.

g) We _____ on very well when we first met.

h) When college finished we all _____ our separate ways and I never saw them again.

3 Fill the gaps by completing the phrasal verb or adding a preposition.

a) Ever since he split _____ with his girlfriend, he prefers to be _____ his own.

b) He was stopped _____ the police and charged _____ possessing a dangerous weapon.

c) I believe _____ love _____ first sight. Do you?

d) She's completely addicted _____ cigarettes and can't do _____ one for more than 30 minutes.

e) We often end _____ watching a soap opera _____ TV because we can't find anything more interesting.

f) You should go _____ of your way to take part _____ more social events.

4 Find partners for the words on the left from the box on the right. Then use these combinations to complete the sentences below.

close	dress
fancy	engagement
full	exam
happy	friend
high	life
mock	moon
previous	note
private	notice
separate	speed
short	ways

a) I'd like to end this talk on a _____ _____ by telling you a funny story.

b) I think I have a _____ _____ but I'll have to check in my diary.

c) I wouldn't describe him as a _____ _____ even though I know him quite well.

d) She failed the _____ but is still hoping to pass the real thing.

e) The school has to find a teacher at _____ _____ when someone is ill.

f) The thieves escaped at _____ _____ in a stolen Ferrari.

g) There was a _____ so we could see quite clearly.

h) After a year of arguments, they decided to go their _____ .

i) They hadn't realised it was a _____ _____ party so they felt very out of place.

j) What I do in my _____ is none of your business.

9 Soap

Quotations

Can you complete these humorous quotations with one of the following words?

| mother   mother-in-law   grandfather   family |

a) All the men in my _____ had beards – and most of the women. (*W.C. Fields*)

b) I haven't spoken to my _____ for eighteen months – I don't like to interrupt her. (*Ken Dodd*)

c) You see this watch? This is an absolutely fantastic, very fine, elegant gold watch which was sold to me by my _____ on his deathbed. (*Woody Allen*)

d) My _____ loved children – she would have given anything if I'd been one. (*Groucho Marx*)

Grammar

1 Match the sentences in box A to their reported equivalents in box B.

A

> She said:
> a) 'I'll always think about you.'
> b) 'I've always thought about you.'
> c) 'I'm always thinking about you.'
> d) 'I always think about you.'
> e) 'I always thought about you.'
> f) 'I was always thinking about you.'
> g) 'I would always think about you.'

B

> She said …
> 1   she had always thought about him.
> 2   she had always been thinking about him.
> 3   she always thought about him.
> 4   she would always think about him.
> 5   she was always thinking about him.

2 Put the following sentences into reported speech and backshift the tenses. You will need to change some of the pronouns.

a) 'It's too late to cancel the wedding.'
She said that _____
_____

b) 'Carmen is still going out with John.'
She said that _____
_____

c) 'Mum, there's something you should know.'
She told her mum that _____
_____

d) 'The speech went really badly.'
She said that _____
_____

e) 'They were holding hands!'
She said that _____
_____

f) 'We've had a terrible day.'
She said that _____
_____

g) 'She'll never speak to him again.'
She said that _____
_____

h) 'I've got a problem I want to discuss.'
She told him that _____
_____

3 Read this summary of the beginning of Scene 1 of *Pacific Heights* and underline the reporting verbs.

Edith asked Daniel how he was and he told her that things weren't good. She asked if he was still thinking about Katy and he admitted that he was. He said that he thought he had got over her but explained that all his old feelings had come back. When his grandmother asked about Daniel's wedding to Annick, he insisted that he had been in love with her when he had asked her to marry him, but now he was wondering about how he felt about her. Edith then suggested that Daniel went away to stay with Dave, but Daniel pointed out that Dave was in Mexico.

4 Put these sentences from *Pacific Heights* into reported speech. Use the reporting verb in brackets.

Example
Katy: 'Daniel, I've split up with John!' (tell)
Katy told Daniel she had split up with John.

a) Daniel: 'Has something happened?' (ask)

_____

_____

b) Katy: 'Well, I just realised that I don't love him.' (explain)

_____

_____

c) Daniel: 'You never know … you might change your mind again.' (suggest)

_____

_____

d) Katy: 'No, it's over – for ever!' (insist)

_____

_____

e) Daniel: 'What was John's reaction?' (ask)

_____

_____

f) Katy: 'Um, I haven't told him yet. I'm going to tell him later.' (admit/say)

_____

_____

_____

g) Daniel: 'So, you can't really say that it's all over if you haven't told him!' (point out)

_____

_____

_____

5 Correct the grammatical mistakes.

a) Mara told that there was something going on between Charlie and Clare.

b) Ella pointed out that Clare she was married to Dave.

c) Mara said that lots of married people do have affairs.

d) Ella asked her how she did know.

e) She replied her that she had heard them talking on the phone.

f) Charlie asked Clare if could he come and see her.

g) Mara said that she have got an idea.

h) Ella asked her what was it.

6 In the 1950s, many people tried to predict what life would be like in the year 2000. These are some of the things they said. Circle the best verb form.

a) By the year 2000, we *will be finding / will have found* intelligent life on other planets.

b) In 50 years' time we *will be living / will have lived* in cities on the moon.

c) Everyone *will have / will be having* their own private helicopter.

d) By the new millenium, scientists *will be discovering / will have discovered* cures for all diseases.

e) In the year 2000, we *won't have / won't have had* to work any more.

f) In the year 2000, we *will be living / will have lived* a life of leisure.

g) People *will have / will have had* more money to spend.

h) In 50 years, people *will not be eating / will not have eaten* meat.

7 Complete the following sentences with the future continuous or the future perfect so that they are true for you.

a) I'll probably _____ before the end of this week.

b) This time next week, I'll ____ _____

_____

c) By the end of next year, I'll _____

_____

d) In ten years' time, I hope I'll _____

_____

e) In the year 2015, I'll _____

_____

Listening and reading

1 📼 Cover the tapescript and listen to this interview with Marko Kovic, an actor who has appeared in many soap operas. Are the following statements true (T) or false (F)?

a) Marko came to London to be an actor. ☐

b) It was his wife's idea for him to become an actor. ☐

c) He had to improve his English before he could work as an actor. ☐

d) Walk-on actors sometimes have to speak. ☐

e) Marko was a businessman before he started acting. ☐

f) He acts in films as well as soap operas. ☐

g) In *EastEnders*, he mugs a businessman. ☐

h) He has never seen *Emmerdale*. ☐

i) He wants to give up his acting work. ☐

2 Find the following expressions in the tapescript and translate them into your own language.

a) it was only later that …
b) they tend to …
c) If only!
d) It all depends.
e) you can make …
f) It's a load of rubbish.
g) I've had enough of …
h) It's not the most exciting work …

How long have you been an actor, Marko?

Only about three years. I came to London about three years ago because my wife is English. When I first arrived, my English wasn't very good, and it was difficult to find a job. Then, someone suggested I become an actor.

But how could you be an actor without good English?

At the beginning, I was just a background artist – it was only later that I got to be a walk-on actor.

What's the difference?

Well, background artists don't say anything. You just see them walking past or standing around at a party or something like that. As a walk-on, the camera may zoom in on you and you may have a line or two to say.

What kind of roles do you get?

I might be just someone hanging around on the street or at a party, but they tend to cast me as a businessman! If only! I'm a party guest in the new James Bond film. And I was a soldier in *Saving Private Ryan*. And if I have a speaking part, they make me into a Russian – a gangster usually! – because of my rugged good looks, or more probably my accent – there aren't many Slovenian characters!

Is it well paid?

It all depends. It starts at about £80 a day, but you can make three or four times more if you get through a difficult casting.

What are you up to at the moment?

Um… tomorrow I'll be filming an episode of *EastEnders* – that's one of the soaps over here. Do you get it in the States? I'll be playing – guess what? – a businessman from a multinational corporation who gets mugged in the street. And then, on Friday, I'll be playing a party guest in an episode of *Emmerdale*. Have you heard of it? I must admit I've never watched it myself, but I suspect it's a load of rubbish!

Anything else?

Yes, there's a lot of work at the moment. By the end of the month, I'll have done maybe eight or nine days of shooting. But I think my English is quite good now, and I'll be looking for some other kind of work next month. I've had enough of sitting around all day waiting to be called for my walk-on. It's not the most exciting work in the world!

Vocabulary

1 Complete these sentences with *say/said* or *tell/told*.

a) She _____ me she was having second thoughts about our relationship.

b) Why didn't you _____ me you were jealous?

c) What will people _____ if I put green streaks in my hair?

d) My parents _____ that I should be more ambitious.

e) The children were _____ to apologise.

f) I promised to keep it a secret, so I can't _____ anything.

g) What does it _____ on that poster?

h) How old were you when you learnt to _____ the time?

i) I didn't want to _____ the truth, so I _____ a lie.

2 Read this paragraph about the *Sunset Beach* soap opera. Underline the verbs which match the definitions below and write the infinitive of the verb next to the definition.

Amy and Mark <u>are going through</u> a hard time at the moment. Mark has been kicked out of his job, and they are running out of money because they have just bought a new house. They were counting on Amy's step-father, Max, to help them financially, but he said he had a cashflow problem. They were going to have a party to celebrate Amy's birthday, but they called it off when they realised how much it would cost. Then, a week ago, Mark ran into Sonia, who he used to go out with. When he told Amy, she was furious, and they argued about it. It took two days for them to make up.

Example
to experience *to go through*

a) to meet by chance _____

b) to cancel _____

c) to have no more of something _____

d) to end an argument, become friends again _____

e) to be forced to leave _____

f) to rely or depend on _____

g) to have a romantic relationship with _____

3 Complete the puzzle using words from this unit.

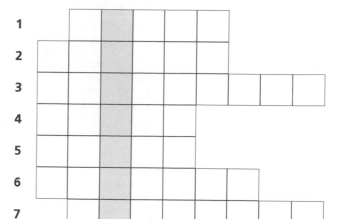

1 your brother or sister's daughter
2 unmarried
3 lipstick, mascara, etc.
4 brothers or sisters born on the same day
5 a woman whose husband has died
6 say what you think will happen
7 your daughter's husband
8 a child of your uncle or aunt
9 stop working at 60 or 65

4 Complete the sentences with an appropriate form of the verbs in the box.

> affect   go   have   leave   mind
> negotiate   run   sign   suffer   take

a) I had always wanted to _____ my own business.

b) I managed to _____ a deal with the bank.

c) Three months after we _____ the contract, the business opened.

d) But in the first few weeks the business didn't _____ well.

e) I was _____ from stress about the money.

f) These worries started to _____ my health.

g) I began to _____ doubts about the restaurant's future.

h) The doctor told me to _____ things easy.

i) But the bank wouldn't _____ me alone and they called every day.

j) One day, I told the bank manager to _____ his own business, and that was the beginning of the end ....

Writing

1 You are going to write a magazine article about Martin Kemp, a star of the BBC soap opera, *EastEnders*. First read the notes about him.

a) Formed a pop group, Spandau Ballet, with brother Gary – very famous in early 1980s – many hits – international tours.

b) Late 1980s – made 'The Krays' with his brother Gary – film (about two London gangsters). Many other films in Hollywood. Decided to return to England.

c) 1984 – met Shirlie (pop singer – sang with George Michael) – married 1989. Happy together. Daughter (Harley), son (Roman).

d) Big fan of Arsenal Football Club – best memory is Arsenal winning 'the double' (Cup and League) – wanted to be a footballer when young – now takes his son to matches.

e) 1996 – brain tumour – serious operation – but recovered.

f) EastEnders (Britain's most popular soap opera – 16 million viewers) – Kemp plays Steve Owen, a club owner – recently murdered his ex-girlfriend – everyone in England talking about it.

2 Match the information above to the categories below.

interests   *d*

films

music

current work

health

family

3 Imagine that Martin Kemp is coming to your town to perform a concert. You work for a local newspaper and you are going to write an article about Martin Kemp. What might interest the people in your town? Is there any information that you do not want to include? Which information would it be a good idea to start with? Make a list to help you plan your article.

4 Choose a title for the article.

Martin Kemp – back from the grave

From football to nightclubs – the world of Martin Kemp

Is there anything that Martin Kemp can't do?

You may be able to think of a better title.

5 Write the article.

Pronunciation

1 Look at these plural words and decide if the **final** *s* is pronounced /s/ or /z/.

birds   clocks   cosmetics   days   daughters
friends   jobs   lessons   students   twins
minutes   months   scales   shops   trips   weeks

/s/	/z/
clocks	birds

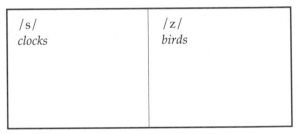 Listen to the recording to check your answers. Then practise saying the words.

2 Think about the underlined letter *s* in these words. Is it pronounced /s/ or /z/?

cri<u>s</u>is   de<u>s</u>igner   di<u>s</u>cuss   exerci<u>s</u>e
increa<u>s</u>ed   co<u>s</u>metics   organi<u>s</u>e   clo<u>s</u>est
plea<u>s</u>ant   pre<u>s</u>ent   que<u>s</u>tion   Thur<u>s</u>day

/s/	/z/
crisis	designer

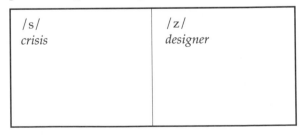 Listen to the recording to check your answers. Then practise saying the words.

10 Time

Time idioms

Complete the following idioms by choosing the best word.

a) Let's call it a *day/second/year*. I'm tired and I want to have an early *afternoon/evening/night*. We can always finish it tomorrow.

b) CNN is well-known for its up-to-the-*second/minute/hour* news bulletins.

c) In westerns, the US Cavalry always arrive at the eleventh *month/hour/minute*. Just when you think that the hero is going to die, the cavalry arrive and save the *moment/time/day*.

Grammar

1 How many phrases can you make from the box below?

	about half	afternoon
	after you	day/Day
at	around	have had a lunch
in	New Year's	July
just	the early hours	of the morning
on	the fourth of	past eight
	the middle of the	the week
	the start of	three o'clock

Now use some of these phrases to write five sentences about things you do.

_____

_____

_____

_____

_____

2 Read the following sentences and decide if they are true (T) or false (F) for your country.

a) You can't drive until you are eighteen. ☐

b) You aren't allowed to drive until you pass a test. ☐

c) You should take lessons to help you pass the test. ☐

d) If you haven't passed your test, you are allowed to drive if a qualified driver is with you. ☐

e) You mustn't drive if you have had more than two glasses of wine. ☐

f) You have to have insurance in case your car is stolen. ☐

g) Older people don't have to pay as much insurance as younger drivers. ☐

h) You shouldn't use a mobile phone when you are driving. ☐

i) You are supposed to drive more slowly in wet weather. ☐

j) You don't have to wear seat belts in the back of the car. ☐

k) You don't have to take a test to ride a motorcycle. ☐

l) You are allowed to ride a motorcycle at any age. ☐

Correct the sentences that are false.

3 Complete these job descriptions with a word from the box.

a)

allowed	can	have	must

I don't (1) _____ to start work at any particular time. I (2) _____ choose because I work for myself. In England, you're not (3) _____ to work for more than eight hours a day because it's dangerous – people get tired. To get a licence, you (4) _____ take a special test to show how well you know the town.

b)

got	have	must	should	supposed

We (1) _____ work at the weekend, but we don't (2) _____ to work every day during the week. We're (3) _____ to have a special diet and we (4) _____ go to bed early, especially if we've (5) _____ to play a match the next day. But not everyone does!

c)

allowed	can't	have	supposed

In my job, you (1) _____ really do anything at all. You just (2) _____ to sit there, watching people, because they're not (3) _____ to touch anything. If they go too close, you're (4) _____ to ask them to move back, but mostly I just try to stay awake. The most important thing is that you don't fall asleep.

4 Write a sentence using the word in *italics*, so that it means the same as the first sentence.

a) 1 It's very important for us to be in good physical condition. (*must*)

We _____

_____

2 It's necessary to follow orders all the time. (*got*)

You _____

_____

3 You can live with your family when you're promoted. (*allowed*)

You _____

_____

4 It's not necessary to wear uniform in the evenings. (*have*)

You _____

_____

b) 1 There's no need to have any special training. (*have*)

You _____

_____

2 You should agree with everything your leader says. (*supposed*)

You _____

_____

3 It's a good idea to be well-dressed. (*should*)

You _____

_____

4 You need to be very ambitious. (*got*)

You _____

_____

5 Label the pictures of jobs and match these jobs to the exercises you have just done.

politician
footballer
museum attendant
taxi driver
soldier

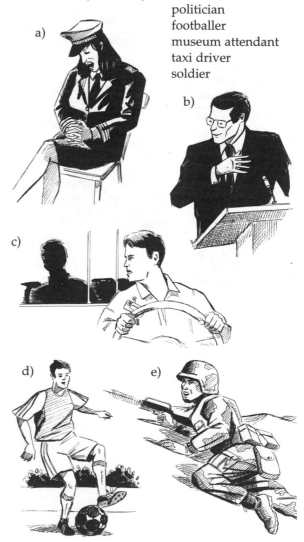

a)

b)

c)

d)

e)

Listening

1 📼 Cover the tapescript and listen to the interview with Dr Lee, an international expert on body clocks. Put the following actions at the best time on the body clock below.

a) avoid taking important professional decisions
b) have dinner
c) drink alcohol
d) go to sleep at night
e) avoid people who are ill
f) make love
g) study
h) play competitive sports like tennis

	1	2	3	4	5	6	7	8	9	10	11	12
AM		a										

	1	2	3	4	5	6	7	8	9	10	11	12
PM												

2 📼 Match a word from box A to a word from box B to make logical combinations. Listen to the recording again to check your answers.

A
- early
- night
- alcoholic
- strictly
- blood
- immune
- contagious
- physical

B
- exercise
- speaking
- cells
- system
- diseases
- hours
- drinks
- shift

I'd like to welcome Dr Lee, an expert in chronobiology, who is with us in the studio this evening. Dr Lee, I wonder if you could begin by telling us what chronobiology is exactly.

Yes, of course. Chronobiology is a relatively young science that studies how the bodies of animals are regulated by a sort of clock that tells them when it is best to perform certain physiological and psychological tasks.

Does this affect humans, too?

Yes, of course. Humans are particularly sensitive to the hormones melatonin and cortisol, which affect how sleepy we are. We have discovered, for example, that in the early hours of the morning, when body temperatures are at their lowest, that we are most likely to make mistakes of judgement – so people like doctors, for example, who often have to work night shifts, need to be particularly careful. We are also very slow – physically, that is – just after lunch, at around three-ish. Our motor reactions are slow so it's not a good time to play tennis, for example.

So the time we eat is very important?

Yes, our sense of taste and smell is at its highest between 6 and 8 pm, so it's not surprising that many people have dinner at that time. They often feel hungry, too, if they've just done some sport.

Does that mean that I shouldn't eat later in the evening?

No, not necessarily, but the stomach doesn't work well at night, so it's best to eat before. However, the liver tends to work better after about 8 pm so that's the best time for alcoholic drinks. Different parts of the body work more at different times of the day – the skin, for example, grows most during the night between 11 and 1, so it's important that we don't go to bed too late.

Are there any other important times we should know about?

Well, at the start of the day, the number of white blood cells you have is low and your immune system is low, so that's a time to avoid contact with people with contagious diseases. But it's also the best time for men to make love!

I'll try to remember that!

The best time for remembering is in the middle of the afternoon – this is when the body is slow but the mind is sharp. If you're learning a foreign language, for example, this is the time to do it, but leave your physical exercise until later. If you want to play that game of tennis, do it after you've learnt those irregular verbs!

Right! And when's the best time for interviews?

Vocabulary

1 Complete these sentences with *time* or *times*.

a) It would save _____ if we took a taxi.

b) Please try to arrive on _____ .

c) At _____ I think you're completely mad.

d) He earns three _____ as much money as I do.

e) We should finish this project in a fortnight's _____ .

f) Take your _____ ; there's no hurry.

g) How many _____ have you been on a diet?

h) How much is twelve _____ seventeen?

i) I think you should stay in your present job for the _____ being.

j) By the _____ they give us a pay rise, we'll all be dead!

2 Look at the following definitions and complete the words by adding the consonants.

a) a person or organisation that buys things from a company
_ _ I E _ _

b) This describes working hours that are not fixed and can change.
_ _ E _ I _ _ E

c) a time or date when you must finish a job
_ E A _ _ I _ E

d) a person that you work with
_ O _ _ E A _ U E

e) a set of information that is stored on a computer
_ A _ A _ A _ E

f) a formal conversation between a company manager and a person who wants to work for the company
I _ _ E _ _ I E _

g) a senior manager in a company
E _ E _ U _ I _ E

h) the property (buildings, etc) of a company
_ _ E _ I _ E _

i) a person who has written a letter asking for a job
A _ _ _ I _ A _ _

3 Combine a word from box A with a word from box B to make compound nouns. Then use them to complete the sentences below.

A
| action |
| casual |
| lunch |
| model |
| overnight |
| working |

B
| agency |
| week |
| clothes |
| hour |
| plan |
| bag |

a) We'll be staying in a hotel so don't forget to bring your _____ .

b) The company has a new _____ to increase sales.

c) We always use a _____ to find new faces for our advertising campaigns.

d) The normal _____ in many countries is 40 hours.

e) Do you stay in the office or do you go out during your _____ ?

f) We don't have to wear anything special to work; we can wear _____ _____ .

Pronunciation

1 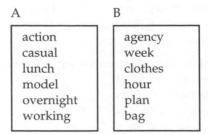 Listen to the recording and put the numbers below into the order you hear them.

a) 6   6th   16th

_____

b) 13th   30th   33rd

_____

c) 9.45   945   9.45 (time)

_____

d) 1.988   1,988   1988 (year)

_____

Now practise saying the numbers.

Writing

1 Read this letter of application for a job.

Dear Sir or Madam,

1 My course finishes at the end of June and I will be free to take up a post after this time. I am available for an interview at any time which is convenient to you.

2 I am twenty-three years old and am in the final year of my course in Tourism Management at South Bank University. During the course, I spent three months on a work placement scheme working for Harrison Guides Ltd as a tour guide, accompanying visitors to Oxford, Brighton and Bath. In addition, I have gained experience of hotel reception, bar and restaurant work during the university vacations. Please refer to the enclosed curriculum for further details.

3 I am writing to apply for the post of tour leader, which was advertised in The Evening Standard yesterday.

4 I believe that I have the appropriate qualifications, experience and personality for this post, and I think that I would find the work stimulating and rewarding.

5 I enjoy meeting people from other cultures and have travelled extensively in Europe. I speak good French and German, and a little Spanish. I am very interested in English history and enjoy sharing my interest with other people.
I look forward to hearing from you.

Yours faithfully,

Matthew Hunt

MATTHEW HUNT

---

2 The order of paragraphs in the letter has been mixed up. Put the paragraphs in the correct order, using the following plan to help you.

paragraph

- Reason for writing ☐
- Qualifications and experience ☐
- Personality and interests ☐
- Summary of reasons for applying ☐
- When the writer is free ☐

3 Complete these sentences or phrases with a word from the box.

as	at	for	from	in	to

a) I am writing _____ reply _____ your advertisement _____ the newspaper yesterday.

b) _____ present, I am working _____ a receptionist _____ the Carlton Hotel.

c) _____ you will see _____ my CV, I have ...

d) I am very interested _____ working for an organisation where I would have the opportunity _____ use my skills.

e) I would be free _____ work _____ your company …

f) I am available _____ an interview _____ your convenience.

4 Write a letter of application for the job advertised here.

CAMP USA

Camp USA,
6 Pride Bld,
Columbia SC 29006
USA

If you are over 18, free to work this summer and have skills to offer on a US summer camp, contact us now.

Journey

Travel expressions

Match the people to the speech bubbles.

a) Check-in clerk at an airport
b) Customer at an airport check-in
c) Customer at a car-hire agency
d) Driver at a petrol station
e) Passenger on a train
f) Ticket-office clerk at a train station

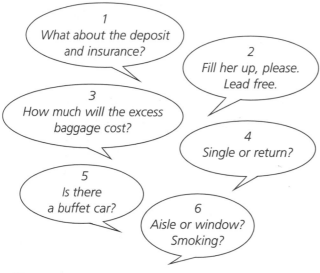

1
What about the deposit
and insurance?

2
Fill her up, please.
Lead free.

3
How much will the excess
baggage cost?

4
Single or return?

5
Is there
a buffet car?

6
Aisle or window?
Smoking?

Grammar

1 Can you name the countries A, B, C? Choose from this list.

Angola, Brazil, Colombia, Cuba, Honduras, Mozambique, Uruguay, Venezuela

Country	A	B	C
Approximate population	22,000,000	156,000,000	11,000,000
Official language	Spanish	Portuguese	Spanish
Climate	tropical	tropical and sub-tropical	semi-tropical
Main exports	oil, sugar, coffee	iron and steel, machinery, coffee	sugar, tobacco, coffee
Highest mountain	5007m	3014m	1974m

A _____
B _____
C _____

2 Complete the sentences with a word from the box.

Country A

can't definitely might suppose

a) It _____ be Brazil because they speak Portuguese there.

b) I think it _____ be Colombia because there are some high mountains there, aren't there?

c) I _____ it could be Venezuela. I think they have lots of oil.

d) It _____ isn't Uruguay, because I'm sure that isn't tropical.

Country B

can't certainly could must

a) It's _____ not Cuba, because that's Spanish-speaking.

b) And it _____ be Honduras – it's not a very industrialised nation.

c) It _____ perhaps be Angola – I think they have a climate like that.

d) It _____ be Brazil. None of the other countries have so many people.

3 Now write four similar sentences about Country C.

_____
_____
_____
_____
_____
_____
_____
_____

4 Read the text and put the sentences in the order in which they happened in Michael Crichton's life.

Michael Crichton, best-selling author of *Jurassic Park*, is one of the world's great travellers. In his autobiography, *Travels*, he describes how he began 'serious' travelling when he was thirty and he went to Bangkok. He then began his extraordinary adventures, which included diving with sharks off Tahiti, observing gorillas in Zaire and living with tribesmen in New Guinea.

It all began in Los Angeles where Crichton was writing films for Hollywood. He had quit his studies at Harvard Medical School and separated from his wife, because he wanted to concentrate on writing. Whilst at Harvard, he had already sold one film, *The Andromeda Strain*, to Hollywood and had begun to lose interest in medicine.

In L.A., he made the successful science fiction film *Westworld*, but he then fell into a depression and did not know what to do next. His first stop was Bangkok, because a friend of his who lived there had invited him. It was the beginning of an incredible odyssey.

a) A friend invited him to Bangkok. ☐

b) He became depressed. ☐

c) He left Harvard. ☐

d) He made *Westworld*. ☐

e) He sold *The Andromeda Strain* to Hollywood. ☐

f) He went to Bangkok. ☐

g) He went to Los Angeles. ☐

h) He went to Tahiti and Zaire. ☐

5 Put the verbs in brackets in these sentences into the past simple or past perfect.

a) By the age of 30, Crichton _____ _____ (already/visit) many countries.

b) He wanted to quit Harvard because he _____ (think) the classes were boring.

c) He separated from his wife before he _____ (go) to L.A.

d) He went to Los Angeles because he _____ (decide) to concentrate on writing.

e) After he went to Los Angeles, he _____ (become) depressed.

f) He remembered that a friend _____ (invite) him to Thailand.

g) When he arrived in Bangkok, his friend _____ (meet) him at the airport.

h) Before he went to Bangkok he _____ (never/be) outside America or Europe.

i) He _____ (know) Steven Spielberg for many years by the time he wrote *Jurassic Park*.

6 Decide if the *'d* in these sentences is *would* or *had*.

a) I'd like to go all around the United States. _____

b) I'd have to work until ... _____

c) ... I'd saved enough money. _____

d) I'd probably travel with a friend. _____

e) If I'd the money now ... _____

f) ... I'd leave immediately _____

g) How much do you think it'd cost? _____

7 Read the following sentences and decide if they refer to past habits (P) or imaginary situations (I).

a) I would hate to go on holiday with him.
b) It would be awful never to have a holiday.
c) My grandfather would never travel abroad when he was younger.
d) My ideal holiday would be on a tropical island with loads of friends.
e) My parents would always take us to London during the school holidays.
f) My nightmare holiday would be two weeks on a coach visiting capital cities.
g) Our family would always go on package holidays because they were cheap.
h) When I was a student, I would always work during the holidays.

Now use the first four words of the (I) sentences and complete them so that they are true for you.

_____

_____

_____

_____

_____

_____

_____

Listening

1 🎞 Cover the tapescript and listen to six people talking about their holidays. (If you don't have the recording, read the tapescript.) Decide if they enjoyed their holiday or not.

Put 😊 or ☹ in the box.

1	2	3	4	5	6

2 🎞 Listen again and match a topic from the box below to each of the speakers.

Topic	Speaker
entertainment	_____
food	_____
hotel	_____
journey	_____
price	_____
weather	_____

3 Decide if the following sentences are true (T) or false (F).

1 a) They didn't like the restaurants or excursions. ☐

    b) They ran out of money. ☐

2 a) The holiday was very tiring. ☐

    b) They sometimes slept during the day. ☐

3 a) The food was disgusting. ☐

    b) The waiters were very friendly. ☐

4 a) The plane was only a little late. ☐

    b) They missed the train. ☐

5 a) They didn't enjoy their first meal. ☐

    b) The restaurants in the town were very good. ☐

6 a) They were unhappy about the snow. ☐

    b) The weather had been better the previous year. ☐

1 The resort was gorgeous with a beautiful sandy beach. The trouble was everything cost a fortune. Restaurants, excursions, windsurfing, jetskis, they had everything, but basically we did nothing at all because we couldn't afford it. After two days we were broke, so we just ate sandwiches after that and watched everyone else enjoying themselves.

2 I was dead by the end of it. I'd always wanted to go, so I thought I'd better make the most of it. We didn't do much during the day because we had to catch up on our sleep, but in the evenings we saw three musicals and then went clubbing to a different place every night. Terrific! I can't wait to get back.

3 Yes, absolutely brilliant. The hotel was a high-rise dump; they hadn't even finished building it. The food was wonderful if you like raw eggs for breakfast, and the service was as friendly as you could expect from a prison camp. It was the perfect destination for your worst enemy.

4 When we got to the check-in they told us there would be a slight delay. Six hours later we finally got on to an ancient plane, and when we were airborne, I just closed my eyes and prayed. When we arrived, we were too late for the train and, in any case, our baggage had got lost somewhere.

5 On the first day, we went down to the restaurant and it was disgusting. Some kind of revolting raw fish with a spicy sauce, ugh! So for the rest of the time we decided to check out other places in the town where we were really spoilt for choice. There were the most amazing places, and we couldn't wait for dinner time to arrive.

6 The funny thing is that although it was freezing, I got really sunburnt. There had been heavy snowfalls just before we got there, so conditions were tremendous. We couldn't have hoped for anything better. I just wish it had been the same last year.

Vocabulary

1 Use the word in brackets to form a word which fits in the gap.

To celebrate our (a) _____ (engage), Suzanne and I decided to have a holiday. At the airport, the plane was delayed and we had to wait in the (b) _____ (depart) lounge. After four hours, we were looking for something to do to relieve the (c) _____ (bored). Then, a very (d) _____ (friend) young boy came over and started chatting to us. He talked and talked, but a lot of what he said was completely (e) _____ (meaning). But he was a funny kid, and we laughed as he talked. Then suddenly, and to our (f) _____ (amaze), he hit me hard on the head. His mother then appeared, apologised and explained that her son was (g) _____ (emotion) unstable, that since his father died he was always looking for attention, but got upset if people laughed at him. We apologised for laughing at him, and Suzanne gave him a kiss when the flight was called. Later in the day, we saw the boy and his mother on the (h) _____ (connect) flight from Madrid. He came over, smiled and hit me on the side of my head.

2 Complete the sentences with a word from the box.

dream	deal	eye	head	break
luck	stretch	board	never	price

a) He's made a fortune on the Stock Exchange but one of these days his _____ is going to run out.

b) I've always hoped that one day I'll be able to live out my _____ of studying in America.

c) I think it's time we took a _____ and did something else.

d) The house was on sale at a very reasonable _____.

e) There were people in all directions as far as the _____ could see.

f) We got there late and had to _____ the flight immediately.

g) Whatever you do, don't lose your _____ – it's important to stay very calm.

h) You've got to decide immediately – it's now or _____ .

i) On busy summer weekends, the traffic jams _____ for miles and miles.

j) Let's make a _____ – pay in cash and I'll take 20% off.

3 Put the words below into the following categories.

airport	aisle	beach
capital	hills	breath-taking
traffic	peaks	flight
gorgeous	jams	fields
picturesque	sandy	spectacular
surf	check-in	waves

Words connected with cities

_____

_____

Words connected with the seaside

_____

_____

Words connected with air travel

_____

_____

Words connected with the countryside

_____

_____

Adjectives to describe views

_____

_____

Writing

1 You are going to write a description of a place that you have visited on holiday recently. Think of a place you have been to.

2 Look at the list of topics below. Tick ✔ the topics that you think it is necessary to include (because they give essential information).
Put a star ✱ next to the topics that you think would be interesting to someone who is thinking of visiting this place.

> What is it called?
>
> Where is it?
>
> How do you get there?
>
> Are there any interesting facts about this place (eg size, population, history)?
>
> Is it famous or popular? Why or why not?
>
> When did you go there?
>
> What time of the year is it best to visit?
>
> What is the weather usually like?
>
> Why did you go there?
>
> What can people do there?
>
> Is there anything to do in the evening?
>
> Are there interesting places to visit nearby?
>
> What kind of scenery or buildings do you find there?
>
> What are the people like?
>
> Are there any interesting places to eat or drink?
>
> Are there any interesting traditions or festivals?
>
> How did you feel about your visit?
>
> What advice would you give to someone who is going to visit this place?

3 You can only write a maximum of 200 words. Select the most interesting topics and make a plan. You should write four paragraphs. Decide which topics will go in each paragraph.

Paragraph 1
Paragraph 2
Paragraph 3
Paragraph 4

4 Look back at your coursebook. Make a note of any vocabulary that you want to include. You might find some of these words useful.

shrines   temples   ruins   high-rise buildings   ski slopes   night life

5 Now write a description of the place you visited. Remember that the person who will read your description is thinking about going there too.

Basics

Basic idioms

Complete the sentences below with one of these idioms:

> eating out of your hand   food for thought
> home and dry   home from home   home game
> lose sleep over it   put to sleep

a) I thought the film really gave you

   _____ .

b) It isn't important enough to worry about: you

   shouldn't _____ .

c) That animal will never recover: it will have to be

   _____ .

d) The boss will do anything you want: you've really

   got him _____ .

e) They were lucky because the last match of the

   season was a _____ .

f) When you get to the end of this book, you will be

   _____ .

g) When we arrived, we saw so many old friends

   that it felt just like _____ .

Grammar

1 Put *a* or *an* before the following words.

   a) _____ CD ROM
   b) _____ European country
   c) _____ FBI agent
   d) _____ honest politician
   e) _____ hungry child
   f) _____ MBA from Harvard
   g) _____ MTV presenter
   h) _____ one-way street
   i) _____ open fireplace
   j) _____ orange juice
   k) _____ ugly building
   l) _____ university department
   m) _____ untidy room
   n) _____ useful piece of equipment

If you use *the* before these words, is it pronounced
/ðə / or /ðiː/ ?

Listen to the recording to check your
answers.

2 Decide in the following dialogues if the nouns
should be singular or plural.

Customer: I'd like some grilled (a) *sardine/
          sardines*, and my husband will have
          your (b) *tuna/tunas* in the
          (c) *garlic/garlics* (d) *sauce/sauces*.

Waiter: I'm afraid we haven't got any
          (e) *fish/fishes* left, madam.

Customer: Never mind, have you got any
          (f) *mussel/mussels*?

Waiter: I'm afraid we've completely run out of
          (g) *seafood/seafoods*.

Customer: Hmm, well, we'll both have the
          (h) *lamb/lambs*. With roast (i) *vegetable/
          vegetables*.

Waiter: We've just served the last of the
          (j) *meat/meats* (k) *dish/dishes*.

Customer: Perhaps, we'll just have a couple of
          (l) *beer/beers* then. Could you bring
          some (m) *olive/olives* at the same time?

Waiter: Certainly. We could do you some
          (n) *sandwich/sandwiches* if you like.

Customer: No, thanks. Oh, and would you mind
          bringing us some clean (o) *glass/
          glasses*? This one smells of old (p)
          cod/cods.

3 Circle the correct verb form.

a) The best pasta *comes/come* from Italy.

b) The sunglasses *costs/cost* me over $200.

c) I bought some bread that *were/was* stale.

d) Your hair *are/is* too long: get it cut!

e) Your luggage *are/is* usually weighed at the check-in.

f) My jeans *are/is* Calvin Klein.

g) Your advice *were/was* extremely helpful.

h) My family *live/lives* all over the world, so we never see each other.

4 Complete the text with *a*, *an*, *the* or – (no article).

(a) _____ worst meal I've ever had was in

(b) _____ restaurant in New York, overlooking

(c) _____ Hudson River. I went there on

(d) _____ recommendation of my brother, who is

(e) _____ banker in New York. He had told me

that they did (f) _____ really delicious seafood.

When we arrived, (g) _____ staff were very

unfriendly and we had to wait (h) _____ ages

before we were taken to our table, which was next

to (i) _____ kitchen. (j) _____ first thing we

noticed was the fact that all (k) _____ plates and

glasses were dirty. There was also (l) _____

horrible smell coming from the kitchen.

5 Complete the text with words from the box.

any	bit	couple	few	little	many
much	no	some			

The waiter came to take our order and we asked
him to come back in a (a) _____ minutes.
When he returned, we ordered (b) _____
mussels to start with, but he said that they didn't
have (c) _____ left. We decided to have the
prawns instead, but then he told us there was
(d) _____ more seafood at all. They had not
bought (e) _____ fish at the market because
they had thought that there would not be
(f) _____ customers. He thought there was
still a (g) _____ salmon, and he went to the
kitchen to check. A (h) _____ of minutes
later he came back and said he had a found a
(i) _____ of tuna. We decided to eat meat
instead.

6 Put *too* or *enough* into each of the following
sentences.

Example   too
The red wine was ⋀ cold – it was almost frozen.

a) We had soup as a starter and it wasn't hot.

b) There wasn't bread and the waiter wouldn't
bring us any more.

c) There was much salt in the pasta.

d) I asked for the meat to be not well-done ...

e) ... but when it came, it wasn't cooked – it was
almost raw.

f) They had put far much garlic in the sauce.

g) The bill was much expensive.

h) We didn't have money to pay.

Pronunciation

1 🔲 Underline the letters that make the /ʃ/
sound in these words. Then listen to the recording
and practise saying the words.

cushions	information
dishes	machine
English	mushroom
expression	reservation
should	spacious
sugar	washing

2 🔲 Look at the following groups of words.
Listen to the recording and notice how the middle
word is pronounced with a /ə/. Practise saying
the phrases.

a cup		milk
a pair	of	jeans
a kind		fish

something		drink
ready	to	go
things		do

problems		work
stay	at	home
dinner		eight

gin		tonic
fish	and	chips
rock		roll

a table		four
late	for	work
food		thought

Reading

1 Read the following article about absinthe and put
   these topics in order.

   a) Absinthe – the latest fashion ☐

   b) How to drink it ☐

   c) The history of absinthe ☐

   d) The reasons for its popularity ☐

   e) What is absinthe ☐

   f) Where you can get it ☐

2 Find words or phrases in the article that you can
   replace with the words and expressions opposite.

Paragraph 1

a) it's quite possible _____

b) strange _____

c) lots of _____

Paragraph 2

d) you can get it _____

e) cost you _____

Paragraph 3

f) to be honest _____

g) drink it _____

h) it had to _____

i) fashionable _____

j) mentions _____

If you go into one of London's most fashionable bars,
there's a good chance that you will see the most
fashion-conscious drinkers with a curious blue-green
drink in front of them. Two new books have been
published on the subject and there are any number of
web pages telling you everything about it. So what is
this new craze that everyone is talking about? Absinthe.

There's nothing new about absinthe. What is new
is that it is available for almost the first time this
century. It will set you back about £10 for a double
shot in a bar, or £40 a bottle through the Internet, but
supplies sell out quickly, and you can't find it in your
local supermarket.

The taste is, frankly, disgusting – a bit like cough
medicine – and you may well wonder why anyone
would want to touch the stuff. The answer is simple –
fashion. A dangerous drink that was unavailable for
many years, and which has been celebrated by painters
like Van Gogh and Picasso – it couldn't really fail to
become trendy. It has other associations, too. Poets like
Baudelaire and Rimbaud were well-known drinkers of
absinthe. Hemingway refers to it in his novels, and was
known to drink it before bull-fighting or running with
the bulls in Pamplona. With a history like that, who
needs advertising?

Absinthe contains 70% alcohol and is made from a
variety of plant products including aniseed. It also
contains a plant called wormwood, and it is this which
has made absinthe infamous. Wormwood is
hallucinogenic and it is said that large quantities of
absinthe will drive you mad.

In Britain it was never very popular, but in France
it was drunk by people of all social classes and it was
banned there in 1915. In the States, the authorities
outlawed it even earlier – in 1912. But after the fall of
the Communist regime in the Czech Republic, a
company called Hill's started making it again, and it has
now found its way back into our lives.

If you want to try it, you pour a measure of
absinthe into a glass. Put some sugar on a spoon and
dip this into the drink so that it is a little wet. Then,
light the sugar, and as it begins to melt, drop it into the
glass. The whole lot will catch fire, so cover the glass to
put the flames out. Add some water, and drink it while
it's still warm. It may make you ill, and it may turn you
blind – but at least you can pretend you're an artist!

Vocabulary

1 Complete the sentences with a word from the box.

> draught   full-bodied   mild   organic
> roast   spicy   strong   wholemeal

a) A lot of people in Britain are buying
_____ food these days.

b) I like a cup of _____ coffee first
thing in the morning.

c) In pubs in Britain, people usually drink
_____ beer.

d) In some countries, it's quite hard to find
_____ bread.

e) Mexican food is often very _____ .

f) My favourite meal is _____ chicken
and chips.

g) Rioja is a _____ wine that goes well
with red meat.

h) Would you like to try this cheese? It's very
_____ .

2 Put the following words into the correct
categories.

> | aubergine | beans | cauliflower |
> |---|---|---|
> | celery | figs | garlic |
> | grapefruit | hake | leek |
> | lettuce | lime | lobster |
> | peach | plum | prawns |
> | raspberries | sausages | turkey |
> | veal | | |

Meat and fish _____

_____

Vegetables _____

_____

Fruit _____

_____

3 Match the words on the left to those on the right.

a) a bunch of   1   advice
b) a carafe of   2   bananas
c) a carton of   3   bread
d) an item of   4   clothing
e) a loaf of   5   humour
f) a pair of   6   luck
g) a piece of   7   milk
h) a sense of   8   paper
i) a sheet of   9   trousers
j) a stroke of   10 wine

4 What are the people talking about? Match the
words in the box to the paragraphs.

> alarm clock   early bird   insomnia
> lie-in   nap   nightmares   snoring
> yawning

a) 'I never get them any more, but I used to
when I was kid. I used to wake up and my
parents had to stay with me until I could get
back to sleep.'

b) 'I would like to have one after lunch – just
half an hour or so, but it's impossible during
the week when I'm at work. I always have
one when I'm on holiday and then I'm less
tired when I go out at night.'

c) 'I can't stand it. I think it's a good reason for a
divorce! I mean, how are you supposed to
find someone attractive if they sound like an
old train? People say you can always put
something in your ears, but I think they
should stick something up their nose!'

d) I always get it when I'm worried or stressed,
and I lie there thinking about whatever the
problem is, but that only makes it worse, so I
get even more worried because I know how
tired I'm going to be in the morning.'

e) 'It's funny, isn't it, because when one person
starts, everyone else starts doing the same
without you realising it. Mind you, it's not
funny when people don't even put their hand
over their mouth.'

f) 'I hate them! When it goes off, I just want to
hit it. And then the day you really want it to
work, the battery runs out and you
oversleep.'

g) 'It's great at the weekend, especially in the
winter, when you don't have to get up and
you can stay warm in your bed. If it were
possible, I'd have one every day.'

h) 'My brother is like that. He gets up at six and
goes for a run or something. He says that he
just can't stay in bed any longer.'

Writing

1 Read this letter of complaint and decide where phrases a) – j) belong.

Dear Sir/Madam,

(1) the meal that I ate in your restaurant last Saturday. (2) both the service and the quality of the food that was served.

I was recommended your restaurant by my brother, who assured me that you specialised in seafood of the highest quality. (3) I learnt that you had no seafood left by the time I arrived. (4), I would not have come. What is more, the food that I was served (5).

(6), the waiters were both inattentive and rude. (7) from an establishment of your reputation. (8) the reason why I feel the need to write this letter. (9) a letter of apology, (10). I enclose the receipt.

Yours faithfully,

T. Wells

T. Wells

---

a) as well as a full refund ☐

b) I am sure that you will understand ☐

c) I am writing this letter to complain about [1]

d) I look forward to receiving ☐ .

e) I was dissatisfied with ☐

f) if I had known ☐

g) this was not what I expected ☐

h) to make matters worse ☐

i) was not of the standard that one might expect ☐

j) you can imagine my disappointment when ☐

2 Look at the advertisement and the notes that you made during your holiday and write a letter of complaint to the managing director of Bellevue Hotels.

Bellevue Hotel
at
Wigan-on-Sea

Call us now to make your booking.
010892 660660
Limited places!

Our room was at the back of the hotel ────────►*Beautiful sea views*

*

Family atmosphere

*

TV and shower in every room ◄──────── The TV didn't work

*

The chef was on holiday! ──────►*Excellent restaurant*

*

Special offers for July ◄──────── When we went to pay, we were told we had to pay an extra summer supplement

*

The children were terrified of a large dog that was always at reception ──────►*We welcome children!*

---

13 Communication

Communicative idioms

Rearrange the words to make idiomatic expressions. Then match the expressions to the meanings below.

a) is it my of on the tip tongue

_____

b) completely for I lost was words

_____

c) about are I know don't on what you

_____

d) mouth my of out the took words you

_____

e) again can say that you

_____

f) are hat talking through you your

_____

1 I completely agree with you.
2 I don't understand what you are saying.
3 I can't quite remember the word I need.
4 You said exactly what I was going to say.
5 What you are saying is nonsense.
6 I was so surprised that I couldn't say anything at all.

Grammar

1 Complete these sentences with *if*, *unless* or *when*.

   a)
   1 We'll go to the beach tomorrow _____ it rains.
   2 _____ we arrive, let's have a picnic.
   3 _____ it's a little cloudy, we could always go for a walk instead of sunbathing.

   b)
   1 Call me on my mobile _____ you are going to be late.
   2 Let's find some time tomorrow _____ we can talk.
   3 I'll see you tomorrow _____ you call to cancel.

   c)
   1 We'll have to get a bigger car _____ the baby is born.
   2 _____ we're lucky, my parents might give us their old one.
   3 They won't help _____ you finally tell them you're pregnant.

   d)
   1 I'd like to live abroad _____ I retire.
   2 I'd like to buy a house near the sea _____ I have enough money.
   3 But _____ I start saving now, I'll never be able to afford it.

2 Rewrite the sentences below, using *unless*.

   a) If you don't hurry up, we'll never get there on time.

   _____

   _____

   b) I can't help you if you don't tell me what the problem is.

   _____

   _____

   c) They have decided to dismiss her if she doesn't resign from the post.

   _____

   _____

   d) We usually go out on Saturday night if we don't have to work.

   _____

   _____

   e) You'll never find a job if you don't try a bit harder.

   _____

   _____

   f) Don't buy it if you haven't got enough money.

   _____

   _____

3 Use the words to write real conditional sentences using *if*.

Example his / mobile phone / ring / again / I go / mad
If his mobile phone rings again, I'll go mad.

a) I / ask / him / switch / off / it / ring / again

_____
_____

b) I / speak / him / you / like

_____
_____

c) what / we / do / he / refuse / ?

_____
_____

d) he / say / no / we / have to / change / seats

_____
_____

e) why / he / not move / he / cause / problem ?

_____
_____

f) why / he / come / cinema / he / want / speak / friends ?

_____
_____

g) he / have / so many / friends / why / he / sit / all alone ?

_____
_____

h) I / ever / buy / mobile phone / I / switch / off / cinema

_____
_____

4 Complete the sentences with an appropriate form of the verb in brackets.

Example
We _____ (get) married in the spring if you like. *We 'll get married in the spring if you like.*

a) Let's get married as soon as we _____ (have) a bit more money.

b) If you don't work harder, you _____ _____ (never get) the promotion you want.

c) I _____ (not have) so much time to spend with you if I get promoted.

d) Nothing's going to happen until you _____ (make) up your mind what you want.

e) If I _____ (not make) up my mind yet, it's because I'm thinking of you.

f) I'll leave you unless you _____ (start) being a little more considerate.

g) If I say 'I love you', _____ (you/change) your mind?

h) If you love me so much, why _____ _____ (you/not phone) me yesterday?

5 Complete the text with words from the box.

also	can	don't	especially	have
if	manage	unless	until	wanted
when	will			

Every afternoon after work, I go home and play *Tomb Raider*. I (a) _____ play it at work, (b) _____ the boss is in the office and I have to be careful. At home, I will usually play for about two hours, but it (c) _____ be longer (d) _____ I am not happy with the progress I (e) _____ made. If I have a problem, I go to a website which gives me the answers, and then I (f) _____ usually carry on playing (g) _____ I have reached the end of a level of the game. There's something very satisfying about finishing a level, (h) _____ if you (i) _____ to do it very quickly. My girlfriend said that if I (j) _____ to spend all my time at the computer, that was my problem, but she had had enough. OK, I said, it's not my fault if you (k) _____ understand me. She couldn't even understand how happy I was last week (l) _____ I finished level 12!

Listening and reading

1 📼 Cover the tapescript and listen to five recorded telephone messages and match them to the places below.

a) a language school
b) a theatre
c) an art gallery
d) a train service
e) a castle

2 Read the messages and decide where to put these prepositions. They are in the correct order.

Message 1: for   from   about

Message 2: to   between   at

Message 3: at   by   in

Message 4: at   on   outside

Message 5: at   about   for

3 📼 Listen to the messages again to check your answers. At the same time, listen and correct any other mistakes in the written messages above.

1 Thank you calling *****, the high speed passenger service. Please choose one of the following four options. To listen to our talking timetable, press 0. To make a booking, press 1. If you are calling an existing booking, press 2. For other enquiries, press 3.

2 This is *****. I'm sorry, but the switchboard is now closed. If you wish to speak an operator, please call this number 8 am and 6.30 pm Monday to Friday. The switchboard is not open the weekends or bank holidays. If you wish to listen to recorded information on *****'s opening times and admission prices, please call 020 7680 9004. I repeat 020 7680 9004.

3 This is the box office at the *****. All our lines are busy the moment. Your call will be answered as soon as possible. We are booking phone and person for performances to 7th July. If you have a touch-tone phone and you would like to hear information on this week's performances and ticket availability, press 1.

4 Thank you for calling *****. Staff will be available to take your enquiry the following times. Mondays and Fridays, staff will be available from 9 am to 7 pm. From Tuesday to Thursday, staff will be available from 9 am to 9 pm. The school will also be open on certain Sundays when you will receive a limited information service. Should you call these times, please leave a clear message after the tone.

5 Hello. You have reached the ***** answering service. I'm afraid that all our operators are busy the moment. For information our current exhibition and full details about Joe Cook, our artist of the month, please press 'star'. For all other enquiries, please hold until an operator becomes available.

Vocabulary

1 Put these telephone conversations into the correct order.

a) ☐ Oh, hi. Listen, do you mind if I call you back? I can't speak right now.

☐ OK. I'll speak to you in half an hour or so.

☐ Sure. I'll be in all afternoon.

☐ Sue? Hi, it's Christine. How are you doing?

b) ☐ Hello. Could I speak to Helen, please?

☐ Yeah, hang on. I'll go and get her.

☐ Is that David? It's Jane here.

☐ 734 4702.

☐ Oh, hi, Jane. Is Helen there?

c) ☐ Yes, could I speak to Mr Read, please?

☐ Accounts department. Can I help you?

☐ Certainly, Mr Lawson.

☐ I'm afraid he's not available at the moment. Can I take a message?

☐ Yes, could you tell him that John Lawson called?

d) ☐ Yes, could I speak to Katy Wright, please?

☐ Yes. Could you say that Markella returned her call?

☐ I'll put you through. I'm afraid her line's busy. Would you like to leave a message?

☐ Macmillan Oxford, good afternoon. Can I help you?

☐ Yes, of course. Could you spell that for me, please?

2 Put *do* or *make* before the following words and expressions.

a) _____ the accounts
b) _____ the bed
c) _____ your best
d) _____ your homework
e) _____ a good impression
f) _____ your mind up
g) _____ a lot of noise
h) _____ a suggestion
i) _____ the washing
j) _____ some work

Now complete the sentences below using one of the expressions above.

1 You've got to _____ : you can't put off the decision for ever.

2 I must _____ : I've got nothing left to wear.

3 I'd like to _____ : why don't we talk about this later?

4 If you don't _____ , you'll never pass the exam.

5 It doesn't matter if you don't win, but try to _____ anyway.

6 It's much easier to _____ if you use a programme like Excel.

7 It's your turn to _____ : it's been me every day this week.

8 The children _____ when they are playing.

9 You really ought to _____ this afternoon or you'll get in trouble with the boss.

10 He didn't _____ on me when I first met him: I thought he was rather stupid.

3 Complete these sentences with an appropriate preposition.

a) Are you any good _____ technical things? My VCR is broken.

b) If you're not _____ to anything this evening, do you fancy going out for a drink?

c) I'm afraid she's _____ the other line at the moment.

d) I'm sick _____ doing these exercises – I'll finish them tomorrow.

e) Sorry I'm late. I had a problem _____ my car.

f) The best thing _____ living in London is all the clubs.

g) What's _____ TV tonight?

h) What time would be convenient _____ you?

i) The bank manager said that I had gone _____ my overdraft limit.

j) I forgot all _____ my worries when I went on holiday.

Writing

1 Two letters have been mixed up. Underline the phrases in the second letter that belong in place of the phrases in italics in the first letter.

NationalBank

16 Market Hill Bristol
Telephone 01702 636 901

Dear Mr Swainston,

We have tried to *catch you at home* by phone *a few times*, without success. I am now writing *about* your current account (A/C No. 78UG437856DH). *We noticed* that this account is currently overdrawn by £1,790.63. *You know* that accounts which exceed the agreed overdraft limit will incur bank charges and the higher interest rate.

If you would like to discuss your financial arrangements with the bank, please call the above number and we will be happy to *fix a date* for you to *have a chat with* a member of staff in our Credit Department. We would be happy to discuss terms and conditions for extending your overdraft limit

We would be grateful if you would *give us a call as soon as you can* to discuss this situation. We look forward to hearing from you.

Love,
Mrs C M Parsons
Personal Banking

2 Look at the expressions below and mark them B if they would be more appropriate in Dick's reply to the bank, or M if they would be more appropriate in his reply to his mother.

a) further to your letter of 21 January
b) sorry for not having been in touch sooner
c) I apologise for not contacting you sooner
d) I've been a bit tied up lately
e) I would be grateful if you would clarify the situation
f) perhaps I'll drop round next week
g) outside your usual opening hours
h) there's no need to worry about me
i) by return of post
j) further details concerning
k) give my love to …
l) thanking you in anticipation
m) let me know if that's OK
n) I hope all is well

3 Now write a reply from Dick to his mother.

The Elms
4 Cross Street
High Brooms
Bristol

Dear Dick,

We've tried to get in touch with you on a number of occasions, but whenever we ring you always seem to be out. Your father said he was a bit worried with reference to you, so I said I would drop you a line. It has come to our attention that you don't call as often as you used to, and we were worried in case you were in some kind of trouble. You will be aware how anxious we get. We don't need to make an appointment, just call round any time and you can speak to us both. You know, we're always pleased to see you. Anyway, do contact us at your earliest convenience, so that we know you're all right.

Yours sincerely,
Mum

Proverbs

Look at these English proverbs. One of them has a different meaning from all the others. Which one?

Never judge from appearances.
You can't tell a book by its cover.
Beauty is only skin-deep.
Every shoe does not fit every foot.
All that glitters is not gold.
Appearances are deceptive.

Do you have similar proverbs in your language? Write them here.

_____
_____
_____
_____
_____
_____
_____
_____

Grammar

1 Complete the conversation with an appropriate form of the verb in brackets.

A: Do you think I (a) _____ (look) good if I wore this for the interview?

B: Hardly! If I (b) _____ (be) the interviewer, I would wonder why you were dressed to go to a party. If I were you I (c) _____ (wear) something more formal, something in a darker colour. You could wear your black skirt if you (d) _____ (buy) something to go with it.

A: If I (e) _____ (have) the money, I would. And if I (f) _____ (have) the time, but the interview is tomorrow. Do you think they (g) _____ (mind) if I (h) _____ (ask) them to postpone the interview?

B: If someone (i) _____ (ask) me if they (j) _____ (postpone) the interview, I (k) _____ (probably say) 'yes', but I (l) _____ _____ (want) to know the reason.

2 Give advice, by completing the sentences.

Example If you got contact lenses, *people wouldn't laugh at your old glasses.*

a) If you sorted out your teeth, girls _____ _____

b) If you got rid of your spots, you _____ _____

c) You would meet more people if _____ _____

d) You might also meet some people if you _____ _____

e) If you got a job, you _____ _____

f) You could use the Internet if you _____ _____

g) If you didn't talk to people about your stamp collection, they _____ _____

h) People might want to talk to you if _____ _____

3 Circle the best verb form.

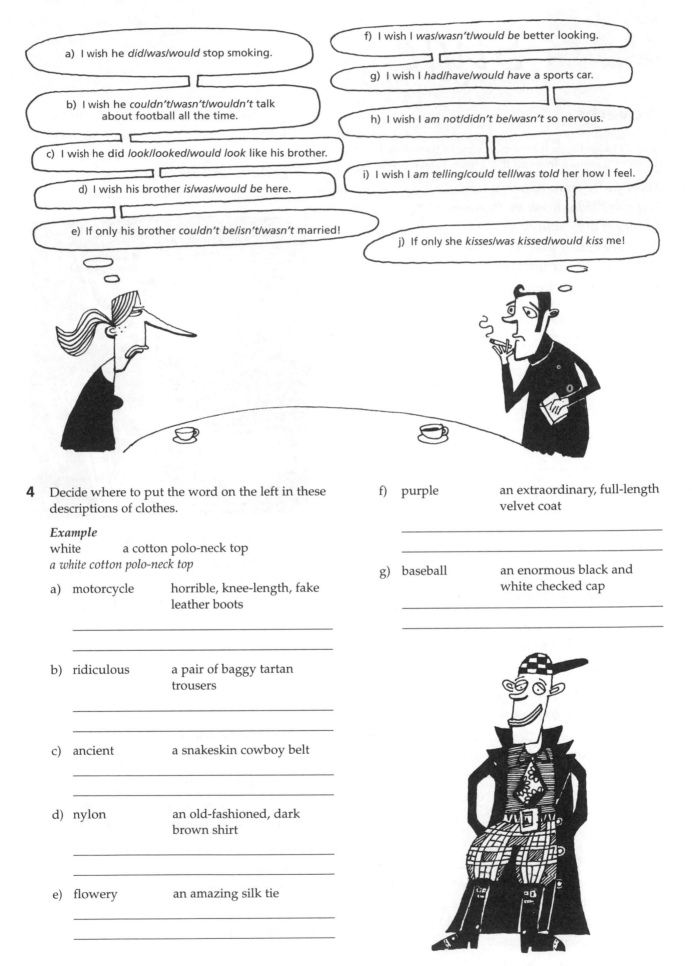

a) I wish he *did/was/would* stop smoking.

b) I wish he *couldn't/wasn't/wouldn't* talk about football all the time.

c) I wish he did *look/looked/would look* like his brother.

d) I wish his brother *is/was/would be* here.

e) If only his brother *couldn't be/isn't/wasn't* married!

f) I wish I *was/wasn't/would be* better looking.

g) I wish I *had/have/would have* a sports car.

h) I wish I *am not/didn't be/wasn't* so nervous.

i) I wish I *am telling/could tell/was told* her how I feel.

j) If only she *kisses/was kissed/would kiss* me!

4 Decide where to put the word on the left in these descriptions of clothes.

Example
white   a cotton polo-neck top
a white cotton polo-neck top

a)   motorcycle   horrible, knee-length, fake leather boots

_____

_____

b)   ridiculous   a pair of baggy tartan trousers

_____

_____

c)   ancient   a snakeskin cowboy belt

_____

_____

d)   nylon   an old-fashioned, dark brown shirt

_____

_____

e)   flowery   an amazing silk tie

_____

_____

f)   purple   an extraordinary, full-length velvet coat

_____

_____

g)   baseball   an enormous black and white checked cap

_____

_____

Listening

1 📼 Cover the tapescript and listen to a journalist talking about fashion designer, Ralph Lauren and choose the best summary of what she says. (If you don't have the recording, read the tapescript.)

Ralph Lauren is so successful because of ...

a) ... his beautiful dress designs.

b) ... the dress he designed for Gwyneth Paltrow.

c) ... his business sense.

2 📼 Listen again. According to the reporter, are the following statements true (T) or false (F)?

a) Some people did not think that Gwyneth Paltrow really cried. ☐

b) Oscars night was not a big success for Ralph Lauren. ☐

c) Ralph Lauren did not train as a fashion designer. ☐

d) Lauren's designs are fashionable and very modern. ☐

e) People in big cities do not wear Lauren clothes. ☐

f) Lauren first sold glasses and plates in a market. ☐

g) Lauren's clothes are too expensive to wear to work. ☐

h) Gwyneth Paltrow's dress was good publicity for his new store. ☐

This week on *Catwalk Talk* we look at one of the biggest names in high-street fashion, Ralph Lauren. Our reporter, Alison Martin, reports on why Lauren is such big news.

After Gwyneth Paltrow had got up to collect her Oscar for *Shakespeare in Love*, there were only two topics on journalists' minds. The first was that she had cried and many felt that the tears were not real. The second was the dress she was wearing – a bright pink taffeta creation by Ralph Lauren.

The Oscar evening was not, perhaps, an unconditional success for Gwyneth Paltrow, but for Ralph Lauren it was a major PR coup. The dress got everybody talking and for a businessman like Lauren, all that talk could only be good news. His company is worth over $2 billion, and Oscar night was just another in his incredible string of successes.

Ralph Lauren studied psychology, not fashion, at college, and it is this perhaps that marks him out from other famous designers. There's nothing especially fashionable about his fashions; his designs are conservative, rather than avant-garde. But he understood very early that style equals lifestyle, and that people are prepared to pay to show the world that they have a particular lifestyle. He had a good eye for clothes and good business sense.

He was the first designer to move into the lucrative sportswear market. Is there any big city anywhere in the world where you can't see people wearing the familiar Lauren Polo brands? He was the first to move into the home furnishings market, so now you can wear Ralph Lauren and live Ralph Lauren, drink from Lauren glasses, eat from Lauren plates, even sleep in Lauren sheets. And he was the first to move downmarket and provide clothes for those of us with tighter budgets. The first to provide stylish, designer label clothes that you could afford to wear to work.

So last week's Oscars were an important night for Lauren. With a new store, his eighth, opening in London's ultra-fashionable Bond Street, what better publicity could he have hoped for?

Vocabulary

1 Look in the word square to find 11 words for clothes and 9 materials. The words are written up and down, left to right and right to left.

Clothes

_____

_____

_____

_____

Materials

_____

_____

_____

T	F	C	A	R	D	I	G	A	N
A	R	A	N	O	L	Y	N	R	F
O	A	S	D	E	N	I	M	A	U
C	C	H	L	E	A	T	H	E	R
T	S	M	T	A	O	C	S	W	S
S	W	E	A	T	S	H	I	R	T
I	D	R	O	C	A	P	L	E	O
A	T	E	K	C	A	J	K	D	O
W	O	O	L	T	L	E	B	N	B
T	E	V	L	E	V	T	I	U	S

2 Match the words on the left to their opposites on the right.

a) ancient   1 old-fashioned
b) fake   2 casual
c) formal   3 loose
d) up-to-date   4 brand-new
e) scruffy   5 real
f) tight   6 smart

_____

_____

_____

_____

_____

_____

3 Find six differences between the pictures.

A

B

Example
B has an earring, A hasn't.

1 _____

   _____

2 _____

   _____

3 _____

   _____

4 _____

   _____

5 _____

   _____

6 _____

   _____

Writing

1 Read this description of a young girl and match the topics to the paragraphs.

paragraph

a) appearance
b) clothes
c) interests
d) personality

My little niece, Lou, is eight years old, and is the spitting image of my sister. I have a photo of my sister when she was the same age and you can't tell them apart. She's got straight fair hair with a fringe, and the first thing you notice about her are her bright blue eyes. She's got a lovely smile.

To begin with she seems quite shy, but when she gets to know you, she never stops talking. Her teachers say she's a real chatterbox. She particularly likes telling jokes, and when she is with her friends they never stop laughing. She's also very generous.

She used to like wearing flowery dresses, but she's gone off them now because she thinks they are too 'girlish'. But most of the time, she just puts on jeans and a T-shirt. If you saw her in the street, you would probably think she was two or three years older.

She's really into girl groups like All Saints. She sings at the top of her voice because she keeps forgetting that everyone can hear her. The only problem with this is that she can't sing to save her life.

2 The following sentences have been cut out of the description. Where should they go?

a) When she finds something funny, it's impossible not to smile with her.

b) I remember one day she had to go into hospital, and when she left she wanted to give all her toys to the hospital for the other kids.

c) Every now and then, she'll wear a dress, but it has to be black and 'grown-up'.

d) When she's not at school, she has always got her Walkman with her.

3 Decide if the following expressions refer to appearance (A), personality (P) or clothes (C).

a) Her smile reminds me of my sister.
b) Like me, she's a quiet sort of person.
c) She can come across as a bit aggressive.
d) She doesn't mind looking untidy.
e) She likes to dress casually.
f) She looks a bit like her mother.
g) She's a bit of a rebel.
h) She's really into Nike trainers.
i) What strikes you first are her eyes.

4 Now write a description of someone you know very well. Organise your description in the same way as the description opposite. Write between 150 and 200 words.

Pronunciation

1 Look at the box of words from this unit that have three syllables. Do they have the stress on the first or the second syllable? Put them into the correct column.

cardigan	exotic	designer	casual
glamorous	romantic	commercial	
probably	expensive	attractive	gallery
obvious			

cardigan Ooo   *exotic* oOo

_____   _____

_____   _____

_____   _____

_____   _____

_____   _____

15 Age

Old jokes

Can you get these jokes?

*   They said the baby looked just like me. Then they turned him the right way up.

*   When I was a kid I was pretty stupid. In fact, I didn't realise I was twelve until I was fourteen.

*   Middle age is when work is a lot less fun and fun is a lot more work.

*   The greatest problem about old age is the fear that it may go on too long.

*   I prefer old age to the alternative.

Grammar

1 Rewrite the sentences below beginning with *I wish …*

> ***Example***
> Why didn't I stop at the traffic lights?
> I wish *I had stopped at the traffic lights.*

On the way home from a fancy-dress party

a) It's a pity the police saw me.
    I wish _____
    _____

b) I shouldn't have drunk so much at the party.
    I wish _____
    _____

c) Why didn't I leave my car at the party?
    I wish _____
    _____

d) I could have asked someone to give me a lift home.
    I wish _____
    _____

e) Or I could have called a taxi!
    I wish _____
    _____

f) Why on earth did I choose such a stupid costume?
    I wish _____
    _____

g) I should have changed before leaving the party.
    I wish _____
    _____

h) It's a pity I went to the party!
    I wish _____
    _____

2 Complete the sentences by putting the verbs in brackets into the appropriate tense.

The morning after the night before

a) If he _____ (not go) to the party, he _____ (not be) in prison now!

b) If he _____ (think) about it more carefully, he _____ (choose) another costume.

c) He _____ (leave) his car at home, if he _____ (choose) another costume.

d) If he _____ (feel) less embarrassed at the party, he _____ (drink) less.

e) His car _____ (still be) outside the party if he _____ (take) a taxi.

f) If he _____ (not jump) the red light, the police _____ (not stop) him.

g) He _____ (be) happy sleeping in his bed if he _____ (not be) arrested.

h) If none of this _____ (happen), he _____ (feel) much happier.

3 Rewrite the following questions beginning *Do you mind if I ask you ... ?*

a) Why are you wearing those clothes?
Do you mind if I ask you _____
_____

b) What sort of party was it?
Do you mind if I ask you _____
_____

c) Do you often dress like that?
Do you mind if I ask you _____
_____

d) Have you got any other clothes?
Do you mind if I ask you _____
_____

e) What time did you leave the party?
Do you mind if I ask you _____
_____

f) Did you know you had drunk too much?
Do you mind if I ask you _____
_____

g) Have you ever been arrested before?
Do you mind if I ask you _____
_____

h) Does your wife know where you were?
Do you mind if I ask you _____
_____

4 Complete these sentences with an appropriate form of the verb in brackets.

a) If this were a hotter country, we _____ (need) air-conditioning.

b) If my alarm clock was working properly, I _____ (not oversleep) this morning.

c) If we hadn't missed the train, we _____ (not arrive) so late.

d) I would have helped you if I _____ (not be) so busy at the moment.

e) If I hadn't spent so much on holiday, I _____ (not be) so short of money now.

f) You wouldn't be feeling so ill if you _____ (not eat) so much last night.

5 Decide if the following sentences are real conditionals (R) that talk about the results of real or possible situations, or unreal conditionals (U) that talk about the results of imaginary or hypothetical situations.

a) I wouldn't wear that if I were you.

b) If you don't like it, why did you buy it?

c) I wouldn't have bought it if you hadn't said you liked it.

d) Well, if you aren't going to wear it, I would like to have it.

e) If I lost a bit of weight, I think it might suit me.

f) If you change your mind, let me know.

Listening

1 🔊 Cover the tapescript and listen to someone talking about young people. Which person do you think is speaking?

a)

b)

c)

2 🔊 Listen to the speaker again and tick the things that he complains about.

a) their appearance
b) They smell.
c) their hairstyles
d) They don't have jobs.
e) They don't want to work.
f) They drink too much.
g) They take drugs.
h) They play computer games.
i) the music they listen to
j) the food they eat
k) They don't vote for the government.
l) They have too much money.
m) They steal.
n) They don't study enough.
o) They don't take life seriously.

Great Bores of Today

I don't know what's happened to the young people of today. I mean just look at them walking around as if they had nothing better to think about than how they look, with rings in their noses and their navels, and they complain that they can't find a job. But, I ask you, would you give a job to someone looking like that? Sometimes, I think they do it on purpose so they don't have to work, but I don't see why they should get social security if they don't make an effort. People just don't seem to have any respect these days. In my day, you'd never see someone drunk on the street, or if you did, the police would lock them up without so much as thinking about it. But these days, you see these kids with their cans of lager, and they probably take drugs, too, there's that crack you keep hearing about, walking down the street as if they owned the place, and the police don't seem to be able to do anything about it. You keep reading stories in the papers about raves where they're all out of their tiny minds on drink or drugs or whatever, and they play some kind of awful music that sounds like interference on the TV set to me. I don't mind a spot of loud music – my wife and I used to love going to rock 'n' roll dances when we were their age – but the stuff you hear these days is just noise. I don't know where they get their money from. They can't be short of it: they must spend a fortune on all those drugs and drink. And where do they find the money for the festivals, I'd like to know. It's a real shame, if you ask me. I'd have loved the chance to go and study at university when I was a young man, and now that there's education for everyone, these people don't seem to want it. It's such a waste, and they'll regret it later. One day, one day, they'll realise that life isn't one long party and there's more important things to think about. Meeting the right person, settling down, having kids: these things matter. You can't go on pretending for ever that it's all a game.

Vocabulary

1 Complete the table and then use a word from the table to complete the sentences below.

noun	adjective
adventure	_____
ambition	_____
anxiety	_____
desperation	_____
disaster	_____
enjoyment	_____
finance	_____
sanity	_____

a) He was the most _____ man I'd ever met: he wanted everything before he was 21.

b) It's difficult to remain _____ when everyone around you is going crazy.

c) The company got into _____ difficulties a few years ago.

d) The holiday was _____ : everything went wrong!

e) There's no need to be _____ : everything will be all right.

f) There's no reason why learning can't be both _____ and serious.

g) They were _____ to have a baby.

h) You ought to be a bit more _____ : why don't you go somewhere different for a change?

2 Complete the sentences with an appropriate form of a verb from the box.

get go have lose make pass take wear

a) After what happened, I'll never _____ his advice again.

b) Building your vocabulary may help you _____ exams.

c) Have you _____ touch with your old friends or do you still see them?

d) How many mistakes have you _____ in this exercise?

e) I'm _____ a bit of trouble finding the answer to this one.

f) If he's not careful, he'll _____ bankrupt.

g) We _____ really wet in the rain yesterday.

h) What kind of perfume do you _____?

3 Find the following words in the word square. The words are written up and down, left to right and right to left.

a) a vegetable often eaten with tomato sauce
_____

b) ask for money _____

c) out of money _____

d) part of a shop where you put your money
_____

e) colours (hair) _____

f) autumn (US) _____

g) enjoyable/enjoyment _____

h) a person who doesn't tell the truth _____

i) you may do this with an ice cream
_____

j) part of a cooker _____

k) a metal container for food _____

l) part of your mouth _____

m) a very large basket on wheels _____

K	E	U	G	N	O	T
C	O	U	N	T	E	R
I	G	E	B	B	K	O
L	N	U	F	E	O	L
L	E	L	I	A	R	L
A	V	T	I	N	B	E
F	O	S	E	Y	D	Y

Writing

1 Rearrange the sentences below to make the first part of a story.

a) I had always wanted to be a photographer, but at first it was hard to find work.

b) It came when I was least expecting it.

c) None of it was what I had dreamt of and I was afraid that it would go on like that forever.

d) Sometimes, I got jobs working for the catalogues of mail order companies.

e) Then, after two years, I got my first chance of a good photo.

f) To begin with, I made my living taking photos of people's weddings.

2 Complete the second paragraph using the pictures and notes to help you. Begin like this:
One day, I was taking photos in the centre of town ...

old man ... chase ... man with gun ...
put out my feet ...

trip ... fall over...

run away ...

You may find the following expressions helpful.

I knew I had to act fast.
I knew I didn't have a second to lose.
As quickly as I could, ...
The only thing on my mind was ....
I was just about to .... when ....
What happened next took me completely by surprise.

3 Now write the final paragraph. Say what happened next to you, the young man and the old man. Begin by completing the following sentence:
If only I had stopped to think, ...

16 Review

Grammar

1 Complete this story by putting one word in each space.

(a) _____ police in Turkey (b) _____ looking for a woman who goes into flower shops, eats as (c) _____ roses as she (d) _____ and then leaves without paying. They say that the public (e) _____ call the police if they (f) _____ her, but warn that she (g) _____ be dangerous. A police spokesman said that it was clear that the woman (h) _____ medical help. 'We are sure that we will catch her soon,' he said, 'and (i) _____ we do, we (j) _____ make sure that she gets the help she needs.' However, (k) _____ angry florist from Istanbul said that he (l) _____ certain that the police (m) _____ have caught her already (n) _____ they had really wanted to. 'They are just not trying hard (o) _____ ,' he claimed.

2 Each of these sentences has one word which should not be there. Cross it out.

a) By this time next week, we will have been being here for over a year.

b) He told to me you were having problems with your computer.

c) You don't have got to do that if you don't want to.

d) We can are allowed to wear anything we like.

e) I'd have finished dinner by the time she arrived.

f) It might not to be very hot when you arrive.

g) There were not hardly any people in the restaurant.

h) We're going on holiday to the France next year.

i) If you will arrive early, give me a call.

j) Don't look at the answers unless you don't find it impossible without them.

k) I wish I didn't had a bit more money.

l) Have you ever had your hair been dyed?

m) If you ask me, your hair is too much short.

n) We wouldn't be lost if you could had brought a map.

3 Use the word at the end of each line to form a word which fits the gap.

Example
She is much too _____ to ask for help.
depend
She is much too *independent* to ask for help.

a) He made a _____ after the wedding.
   speak

b) The demonstration turned to _____ .
   violent

c) I was born on the _____ of June. *thirty*

d) Mandela waited many years for his _____ . *free*

e) Many people think that _____ chocolates are the best in the world. *Belgium*

f) He arrived very _____ so we weren't ready at all. *expect*

g) Some people say that computer games are dangerous and _____ . *health*

h) I think you should get that knife _____ . *sharp*

4 Rewrite the second sentence so that it has a similar meaning to the first sentence, beginning with the words given.

a) 'Did you see the latest episode of *Pacific Heights*?' she asked me.
   She asked me if _____
   _____

b) This is my fifth year of studying English.
   By the end of the year, _____
   _____

c) It's not necessary to answer every question.
   You _____
   _____

d) What should we do if we don't understand?
   What are _____
   _____

e) I expect you speak English well after your
course.

You must _____

_____

f) If you're not interested, you probably won't
learn much.

Unless _____

_____

g) I really shouldn't have had my nose pierced.

I wish _____

_____

h) She advised me to find a new hairdresser.

'If I _____

_____

i) It's a good thing we left early or we would
have missed the train.

If we _____

_____

j) I'm sorry that I didn't remember his name.

If only _____

_____

5 Find a response in box B to the conversational
remarks in box A.

A

> a) Are you bringing Philip to the party?
> b) Could you give me a hand with this?
> c) Have you kissed him yet?
> d) How late is it?
> e) Let's do it just one more time.
> f) Let's meet for a drink before the film.
> g) What time shall we meet before the film?
> h) Where's the bottle-opener?
> i) Would you like some water in that?
> j) You look tired out. What have you been
>   up to?

B

> 1 Hang on! I'll finish what I'm doing.
> 2 Haven't you heard? It's all over.
> 3 What a day! Where shall I start?
> 4 Look! Over here.
> 5 Mind your own business.
> 6 No, I'm sick of it.
> 7 Not a bad idea. In the Metropole?
> 8 Say, half six, in the bar?
> 9 Thanks. Just a drop.
> 10 Just gone twelve.

Pronunciation

1 🔊 Listen to these phrases. Notice how an extra
sound is put between two vowel sounds.

to /w/ a party   me /j/ and you

Now listen to the following phrases and write the
extra sound, /w/ or /j/.

a) be /_____/ able to
b) go /_____/ on holiday
c) he /_____/ admitted
d) so /_____/ I did it
e) tea /_____/ and biscuits
f) the /_____/ enclosed form
g) three /_____/ or four
h) through /_____/ a hard time
i) to /_____/ interrupt him
j) two /_____/ orange juices

Listen again and practise saying these phrases.

2 🔊 Listen to this phrase. You will hear it twice.

He won't be able to do it

The first time the voice went down at the end.
This shows that the sentence is complete. The
second time the voice went up at the end. This
shows that there is more information to come.

Listen to the following phrases and decide if they
are complete or not.

a) We're planning to go on holiday
b) He admitted driving without a licence
c) Nobody would help me so I did it
d) She likes to have tea and biscuits
e) Please complete the enclosed form
f) I've asked him three or four times
g) She's been going through a hard time
h) It's not a good idea to interrupt him
i) I'd like two orange juices

Practise saying the complete sentences.

Now complete the other sentences with one of the
following phrases and practise saying them.

1 or insurance   4 since the divorce
2 at four o'clock   5 and a Coke
3 and return it today

Vocabulary

1 Circle the correct word.

a) Do you still *expect/wait for* him to arrive?

b) He's probably in his *mid/middle* thirties.

c) I don't think those trousers really *fit/suit* you:
they make you look too serious.

d) I met my *ancient/former* boyfriend the other day.

e) I'd *prefer/rather* stay at home, if you don't mind.

f) If the police ask you any questions, just *deny/refuse* everything.

g) It's a shame that so many couples have *arguments/discussions* about the housework.

h) She's going to try *breaking/to break* the world record in her next race.

i) We should be able to do this on time because there are still *few/several* days left.

j) Will you *remember/remind* me to lock the door when we leave?

2 Complete the sentences below with a word from the box.

> did   got   had   held   made   put
> said   served

a) He _____ dressed as quickly as he could.

b) I _____ the homework exercises as soon as I got home.

c) I _____ on for five minutes but then the line went dead.

d) If you ask me, it _____ him right.

e) She thought she loved him, but she _____ second thoughts when she got to the church.

f) The party was _____ off until next weekend.

g) They _____ such a noise that we couldn't hear ourselves speak.

h) You shouldn't have _____ a word about this to anyone.

3 Fill the gaps by completing the phrasal verb or adding a preposition.

a) He applied _____ a job _____ response to an advert in the newspaper.

b) He arrives at work _____ time about once a week _____ average.

c) I'd like to be more _____ to date but I'm not very good _____ choosing new clothes.

d) I live in a little village _____ the mountains just _____ the north of the city.

e) She got engaged _____ her boyfriend _____ New Year's Eve.

f) The operator couldn't put me _____ because the person I wanted to speak to was _____ another line.

g) I'm sick _____ waiting for them – I don't think they'll ever show _____ .

h) My alarm didn't go _____ this morning and it completely messed _____ my plans for the morning.

4 Find partners for the words on the left from the box on the right. Then use these collocations to complete the sentences below.

constant	chocolate
strong	looks
higher	education
opposite	family
nuclear	coffee
plain	practice
reasonable	pressure
second	price
standard	sex
good	thoughts

a) Do you prefer _____ or the kind made with milk?

b) He doesn't seem to understand that his _____ will go as he gets older.

c) He is completely incapable of having a relationship with a member of the _____ .

d) He's under _____ from his family to find a job.

e) I like a cup of _____ in the morning to wake me up.

f) It is _____ to have an answer key at the back of the book.

g) She said she would marry him but she's having _____ .

h) There are more opportunities for _____ in many countries these days.

i) With fewer people getting married, the _____ may be a thing of the past.

j) You can often find tickets to New York at a very _____ .

Answer key

1 Friends

English expressions

a) Diamonds are a girl's best friend.
b) With friends like that, who needs enemies?
c) A friend in need is a friend indeed.

Grammar

1 a) When 2 b) Whose 8 c) Who 1
d) Where 6 e) Why 5 f) What 3 g) – 7

2 a) no preposition needed b) with c) to
d) about e) with f) to
g) no preposition needed h) between

3 a) Did you see b) happen c) happened
d) was it e) did they want

4 A: Did you see 'Friends' on TV last night?
B: Why? Did anything special happen?
A: Well, you remember that Rachel got angry with Ross when they were playing cards?
B: Yes ...
A: Well, the next day he invited her out to dinner ...
B: What happened?
A: She was just telling him that she wanted to be with someone else when, in through the door ...
B: ... his ex-wife arrived!
A: No!
B: Who was it? Her boyfriend?
A: No, it was Chandler and the others.
B: Oh no! What did they want?
A: Well, it was quite funny – no, I tell you what, I'll lend you the video.

5 1 How many times *can you* fold a piece of paper? a) 7

2 Who was the first CD in the US recorded *by*? / Who *recorded* the first CD in the US?
   c) Bruce Springsteen

3 How much lipstick *does* the average woman *use* in her lifetime? c) 2.5 kg

4 Which singer did the Wailers play *with*?
   b) Bob Marley

5 How much *does* your brain *weigh*? a) 1.5 kg

6 *Whose* real name is Annie Mae Bullock?
   b) Tina Turner

7 How many birthdays does the Queen of England *have*?
   b) 2 (her real birthday and her official birthday)

8 Which companies *made* the first CD?
   a) Philips and Sony

9 *Which* countries was the shortest war in history between? c) England and Zanzibar

10 Which country *won* the first World Cup?
   b) Uruguay

6 a) Who was John Lennon married to?
Answer Yoko Ono.
b) When was John Lennon killed?
Answer In 1980.
c) Who does Keith Richards write songs with?
Answer Mick Jagger.
d) What have Carol King and the Brand New Heavies got in common?
Answer They both recorded the song *You've got a friend*.
e) Whose mother came from Nicaragua?
Answer Jade Jagger's.
f) Which French singer made *Je ne regrette rien* famous?
Answer Edith Piaf.

7 a) Which company bought Rolls Royce in 1998?
b) Which song did Elton John sing at Princess Diana's funeral?
c) Who trains Aranxta Sanchez?
d) Who does/did Madonna play in the film *Evita*?
e) What opera did Verdi write in 1853?

Pronunciation

1 a) short: perhaps, salary, thank
long: army, father, start

b) short: because, common, model
long: called, fall, noughts

c) short: killed, lived, women
long: dream, people, ski

d) short: dead, friend, rest
long: earn, first, hurt

2 short: a), c), d), e)
long: b), f), g), h)

3

born	nought	fall
hurt	earn	world
soul	chose	smoke
whose	choose	truth
won	love	come

4 a) What did you do that <u>for</u>? *strong*
I did it <u>for</u> you! *weak*

b) Who did you send the letter <u>to</u>? *strong*
I sent it <u>to</u> the director. *weak*

c) What are you looking <u>at</u>? *strong*
I'm looking <u>at</u> the instructions. *weak*

d) What were you thinking <u>of</u>? *strong*
I was thinking <u>of</u> the day we met. *weak*

Reading

1 a) T   b) T   c) F   d) F   e) T   f) F
g) F   h) F

2 *Recorded music*
track, album, recording, single, release, hit, disc
Kinds of music
soul, funk, indie, acid jazz, R & B (rhythm and blues), hip hop, rap, instrumental, ballad

3 a) option   b) rehearsed   c) ecstatic   d) debut
e) founder   f) invaded the airwaves
g) a string of   h) solo   i) to date

Vocabulary

1 a) split up   b) gone our separate ways
c) hit it off   d) had a lot in common
e) were very close   f) drift apart
g) started seeing   h) going out   i) getting on
j) missed her   k) ended up   l) get back together

2 *adjectives:* friendly, unfriendly, friendless
nouns: friendliness, unfriendliness, friendship

3 a) play for a team   b) tell the truth
c) share a flat   d) earn a good salary
e) join the party   f) appear in a film
g) work for a company   h) make friends

Writing

2 I can't understand English TV. I think that watching TV is a good way to *improve* my English, but I can't understand most programmes. Does anyone *know* a *satellite* or cable programme that is good for intermediate students? Nothing boring, please!   *Andrej, Poland*

MUSIC! MUSIC! MUSIC!
Sing and learn English! Do you want to *exchange* English song lyrics? Tell me what you're into and we'll see if our *tastes* match. What *interests* you?   *Valentina, Italy*

I speak a little English but I want to start classes at a *language* school. There are hundreds of schools in my city and I don't know how to *choose*! What should I look for? What sort of questions *would you* ask?
Waldemar, Brazil

Hi! My name's Natalia. I'm thinking of going to America or *Britain* next *autumn* for an English language course. *How do/should* I start looking for

a good school? Can anyone help me? *Natalia, Argentina*

HELP! I've got an English exam next month and my *grammar* is not so good. Who *knows* a good English textbook with practice *exercises*? Who publishes it?
Markus, Switzerland

PS I've got the blue book and I've finished it already.

2 *Relax*

Useful tips(!)

The Little Book of Calm: b), c), f)
The Little Book of Stress: a), d), e), g), h)

Grammar

1 a) I *rarely* have time to read novels these days.

b) I am *normally* too tired in the evenings to do anything except watch TV.

c) People *often* give me books at Christmas and I like to read them in the holidays.

d) People in Britain *frequently* read the newspaper while they are having breakfast.

e) My boyfriend *always* reads the newspaper on the way to work, but he usually just looks at the sports pages.

f) My boyfriend and I *normally* go to the cinema twice a month, but sometimes we go every week.

g) We *hardly ever* eat in restaurants, but we often get a take-away Chinese meal.

h) *Once a month*, usually on a Saturday morning, I take the children to the cinema.

2 a) loves   b) is looking   c) is trying   d) gets
e) takes   f) eats   g) does   h) is thinking

3 a) How often *do* you look at yourself in the mirror?

b) I *have* never had a massage.

c) It's the best film I *have* ever seen.

d) She *has* already got too many appointments.

e) She *does* not need another appointment to worry about.

f) The book *has* sold over two million copies so far.

g) When one child *is* screaming, I don't feel calm.

h) *Are* you reading anything interesting?

4 a) 4   b) 5   c) 1   d) 3   e) 6   f) 2

5 a) is getting   b) has always supported
c) does not believe   d) wants   e) has started
f) does not want   g) has already started
h) is finding

6 a) works b) produces c) gives
 d) has become   e) has already published
 f) has sold   g) has appeared   h) is increasing
 i) has become / is becoming   j) write
 k) is working   l) is trying

Listening and reading

1 a) 3 b) 2   c) 1

2 1 *The Woman Who Disappeared*   2 *Jurassic Park*
 3 *Oliver Twist*

3 1   Just then, the door opened behind
  me. Jo and his tall friend stood in the
  doorway, and the tall man was holding a gun.
  There was a loud bang as the gun went off.
  The bang was followed *by* a scream of pain
  from one of the cooks, because the tall man
  had shot him in the foot by mistake.
  I quickly picked up a large pile of dirty plates
  and threw them *at* Jo. He saw the plates
  coming and he tried to move *away*. As he
  moved, he slipped on the floor and fell *onto* a
  pile of broken plates.
  Without waiting, I ran to a door at the back of
  the kitchen. The door was locked and I
  banged *against* it with my shoulder. The lock
  broke easily and I pushed the door open. As I
  ran out into the dark street, I could still hear
  the shouts and cries coming from the Club.

 2   As they walked, they heard the roar of an
  animal. The hadrosaurs *by* the lake were
  suddenly worried. They started to run and
  cry out *in* fear. Then, *with* a terrible roar, the
  adult rex ran *out of* the trees by the lake. It
  chased the hadrosaurs. Grant, Lex and Tim
  ran *towards* some rocks and started to climb
  them. The ground shook. The huge, five-
  tonne hadrosaurs ran round them, crashing
  and trumpeting. Grant waited till the
  hadrosaurs had run past. Then he made the
  children climb the nearest tree. They could
  hide there until he was sure the tyrannosaur
  had gone.

 3   The old gentleman went *on* reading. He had
  grey hair and wore gold spectacles. He wore a
  long, dark green coat and white trousers. The
  Dodger moved nearer. The next moment, the
  old gentleman's silk handkerchief was *in* the
  Dodger's hand. The Dodger and Charley ran
  and hid *in* the doorway *of* a house. The old
  gentleman touched his pocket. He turned
  round quickly. 'That boy's got my
  handkerchief!' he cried.

Vocabulary

1 a) depressed 4   b) confused 6   c) depressing 1
 d) annoyed 10   e) relaxing 8
 f) embarrassing 3
 g) tired 2   h) excited 7   i) boring 5
 j) interesting 9

2 a) into b) into c) over d) for e) under
 f) by g) on h) in i) in j) for k) from
 l) about

3 a) 8 b) 1 c) 5 d) 4 e) 3 f) 2 g) 7
 h) 9 i) 6

3 Dating

Quotations

a)   marriage (5 – Princess Diana)
b)   youth, experience (2 – Brigitte Bardot)
c)   kiss, face (1 – Isabelle Allende)
d)   love (4 – Cher)
e)   boyfriends (3 – Naomi Campbell)

Grammar

1   summary c)

2
infinitive	past simple	past participle
be	was / were	been
find	found	found
get	got	got
give	gave	given
leave	left	left
meet	met	met
ring	rang	rung
say	said	said
see	saw	seen

3 a) 've met   b) gave   c) think
 d) Have you seen   e) Has he telephoned
 f) called   g) didn't say   h) do you think
 i) 've seen   j) saw

4 a) for b) since   c) since   d) for e) since
 f) for   g) since   h) for

5 a)   Vincent has known Chiyo for about six
  months.
 b)   Vincent fell in love with Chiyo six
  months ago. / Vincent has been in love with
  Chiyo for six months.
 c)   Chiyo has had Vincent's umbrella since the
  party.
 d)   Vincent has wanted to ask Chiyo out since
  she took him home.
 e)   Vincent has seen Chiyo a number of times
  since he first met her.
 f)   One of Chiyo's friends told Vincent about her
  departure for Japan a week ago.
 g)   Chiyo has been in Japan since Tuesday.
 h)   Vincent has tried to write to Chiyo for a few
  days. / Vincent tried to write to Chiyo a few
  days ago.
 i)   Chiyo waited / has waited for Vincent to ask
  her out for six months.

Pronunciation

1 *One syllable*: helped, kissed, liked, scared, stressed, tried, thanked
Two syllables: ended, hated, needed, waited, wanted
The words with two syllables all end in /ɪd/. The words with one syllable end in /d/ or /t/.

2
a) I've always wanted to go *to* Bali.
b) She's been married *for* nearly a month.
c) It wasn't love *at* first sight.
d) She's known him *for* a couple *of* years.
e) We didn't learn *from* our mistakes.
f) She's always had a strong sense *of* family.
g) Didn't you see Jack *at* the weekend?

3
a) He isn't exactly <u>patient</u>.
b) She isn't particularly <u>sensitive</u>.
c) They're not what you'd call <u>intelligent</u>.
d) He isn't especially hard-<u>working</u>.
e) She's not very <u>generous</u>.
f) They're not exactly open-<u>minded</u>.

Listening and reading

1 Picture b)

2 a) 3 b) 8 c) 1 d) 5 e) 2 f) 4 g) 6 h) 7

Vocabulary

1 *Suggested answer*
A and H   B and D   C and G   E and F

2

	opposite
broad-minded	narrow-minded
modern	old-fashioned
modest	big-headed
out-going	shy
quiet	talkative
relaxed	stressed out
sincere	two-faced
thick-skinned	sensitive
ugly	handsome
unfaithful	loyal

3 a) 6 b) 5 c) 7 d) 8 e) 3 f) 1 g) 2 h) 4

Writing

1 a) 6 b) 3 c) 2 d) 1 e) 4 f) 5 g) 7

2 a) 7 b) 5 c) 8 d) 3 e) 6 f) 1 g) 2 h) 4

---

4 Adrenalin

Grammar

1 a) 4 b) 3 c) 2 d) 1

2
a) was reading, saw
b) phoned, booked
c) began
d) made/were making, felt/was feeling
e) was, was going
f) opened, jumped
g) was falling, felt
h) thought, was working

3 a) 4 b) 2 c) 1 d) 3

4
a) was seeing → saw
b) was looking → looked
   was seeing → saw
   was shouting → shouted
c) was waving → waved
   was jumping → jumped
d) was opening → opened

5 a) were looking b) was c) thought
d) have been e) arrived f) jumped
g) was smiling h) cheered i) have thought

6 a) have you been b) started c) was studying
d) gave e) have always enjoyed f) said
g) have you done h) have never had
i) Have you ever thought j) have promised

7 a) the most exciting b) the most enjoyable
c) easier d) better e) further, more expensive
f) worse g) the most beautiful h) the best

Vocabulary

1 *Sport*: match, boxer, parachute, fight, skydiver, tennis, surfer
The body: blood, bone, elbow, heart, jaw
Animals: bee, snake, spider

2 A amazing, brilliant, fantastic, incredible
B enjoyable, exciting, interesting, lucky, nervous

3 a) 3 b) 5 c) 4 d) 2 e) 1 f) 6

Listening

1 a) 2 b) 4 c) 1 d) 3

2 a) T b) F c) T d) F e) F f) F g) T
h) F

Pronunciation

Weak
1 I *was* thinking of going skydiving.
2 We *were* beginning to feel nervous.
3 She *has* never been hurt in a fight.
4 *Have* you ridden a horse?

Strong
1 *Were* you?!
2 I *wasn't!*
3 Well, I *have!*
4 No, but my wife *has.*

5 Kids

Grammar

1 a) that/who b) that/which c) whose
d) that/which e) that/who/whom
f) when g) that/which h) where
Sentences d), e) and g) do not need a relative pronoun.

2 a) who's b) Who's c) Whose d) whose
e) who's f) whose

3 a) It's a lawyer who decides if someone is guilty or not.
b) It's a time when the leaves start to fall.
c) It's a kind of doctor that looks after animals.
d) It's an animal that lived in prehistoric times.
e) It's a qualification that you get when you finish university.
f) It's a person who is studying at university.
g) It's a kind of hat that you wear for baseball.

4 You can omit the relative pronoun *that* in sentences e) and g).

5 a) judge b) autumn c) vet d) dinosaur
e) degree f) undergraduate/student
g) baseball cap

6 a) Dad lives with a new girlfriend that/who/whom I don't like.
b) She has a daughter whose name I can't remember.
c) They have a house by the sea which/that I went to / where I went on holiday last year.
d) My mum and I live in a small flat which/that doesn't have a garden.
e) Mum has a job which/that she really loves.
f) She works in the morning when I am at school.
g) I have a friend whose mother works at the zoo.
h) This is a picture of my dad which/that I drew.

7 a) I *always used to be* in trouble when I was a child.
b) I *used to arrive* at school late every day.
c) I *never used to be* any good at my studies.
d) During break times, my friends and I *used to smoke* cigarettes behind the school.
e) One day, we were caught smoking. (no change)
f) We *used to be* very rude to the teachers.
g) All the teachers *used to hate* us.
h) I *used to have* very long hair and *wear* one earring.
i) I *used to think* that school was a waste of time.
j) Eventually, I was asked to leave the school. (no change)

In sentences b) and d) *used to* could be changed to *would*.
b) I would arrive at school late every day.
d) During break times, my friends and I would smoke cigarettes behind the school.

Vocabulary

1 a) alligator b) shark c) toddler d) professor
e) shiver f) autumn g) audience h) burglar
i) subtitles j) turtle

2 a) for b) at c) in d) to e) on f) down
g) across h) off

3 a) 1 b) 14 c) 8 d) 3 e) 16 f) 10 g) 4
h) 9 i) 5 j) 12 k) 2 l) 11 m) 6 n) 15
o) 7 p) 13

Listening and reading

1 a) 3 b) 6 c) 7 d) 4 e) 9 f) 2 g) 8
h) 1 i) 5

2 a) didn't have a clue
b) give you a hard time
c) there was still no sign of her
d) there was nothing for it but
e) as good as gold

3 I think that the worst experience that I have ever had was in my first year of teaching, and the kids knew that I didn't have a clue how to control them. I was giving the students a French test, a subject *that* most students hate. I had this class of third years – they're the worst, children who do anything *that* they can to give you a hard time, spotty adolescents. It's the age-range *that* I hate most.

Writing

1 b) 2 i) 3 f) 4 c) 5 h) 6 e) 7 d) 8 a) 9 g)

---

6 News

Headlines

1959   Batista Flees From Country: Havana Casinos, Shops Looted
1973   Pinochet Takes Power in Coup D'Etat
1975   Spanish Monarchy Restored
1963   Kennedy Assassinated: Is Shot Down in Car by a Hidden Sniper
1950   North Korea Invades South Korea
1961   Russia Fires First Astronaut Into Space

The following are passive structures:
Shops Looted   Spanish Monarchy Restored
Kennedy Assassinated: Is Shot Down

Grammar

1 acquit – acquitted   hide – hidden
ban – banned   hurt – hurt
bring – brought   keep – kept
cancel – cancelled   shoot – shot
choose – chosen   spy – spied
drink – drunk   throw – thrown

2 a) was arrested   b) was stopped
c) were found   d) has been arrested
e) has never been convicted   f) was kept
g) has been cancelled   h) is believed

3 a) is stared at   b) will be paid   c) was stolen
d) has been charged   e) was sacked
f) have been acquitted   g) is protected
h) will be splashed

4 a) discovered   b) was arrested   c) put
d) was shot   e) was jailed   f) made

5 a) keep   b) was   c) seen   d) had   e) gave
f) attacked   g) broke   h) taken   i) given
j) saw   k) broken   l) really   m) kept
n) be   o) been

Vocabulary

1 a) The government took pity on the victims of
the drought.
b) The machine is dangerously out of control.
c) The police car chased them at high speed
d) The president is not available for comment.
e) The thieves were sentenced to ten years in
prison.
f) The victims will receive $5000 in
compensation.

2 a) supporter   b) invasion   c) murder
d) promotional   e) protective   f) judge
g) aggressive   h) destruction

3 a) cry   b) married   c) leave   d) help
e) chased   f) split up

Pronunciation

1 a) ball   b) hard   c) half   d) field   e) student

Listening and reading

1 Anna B   Rod B   Mike A   Wendy A   Steve B
Andy A   Diane A   Alice A

2 a) go along with   b) do without   c) give up
d) make up   e) look up to   f) breaks down
g) find out   h) keep on   i) look forward to

Writing

1 a) although   b) However/Nevertheless
c) despite   d) However/Nevertheless
e) Despite   f) Although

---

7 Party

Party, party

1 d) A third party is a person involved in a legal
case, but not one of the main people involved.
You need third party insurance for your car in
case you accidentally hurt someone. A stag
party (for men) and a hen party (for women)
usually take place immediately before a
wedding.

2 c) A tea party – an afternoon party when people
drink tea. A guilty party is a guilty person, a
search party is a group of people who are
looking for someone who is lost, and a
working party is a group of people who are
working together to solve a problem.

3 b) A host is the person who invites people to a
party. A function is a very formal party, a rave
is a party where there is a lot of dancing, and
a reception is a party after a wedding.

4 a) 'Assisted' means 'helped'. If you gatecrash a
party, you go to a party that you have not
been invited to. If you throw or hold a party,
you organise it: it is your party.

5 d)
6 d)

Grammar

1 a) 5   b) 7   c) 1   d) 9   e) 2   f) 8   g) 6   h) 4
i) 3

2 1B: Maybe. I'll ~~to~~ let you know when we've fixed
the date.
2A: Where ~~you are~~ *are you* going to
find the money?
3B: Yes. I've decided that I'm going *to* write a
letter every morning.
4B: No, don't. I'*m* going to be out tomorrow.
5B: Yes, I'll ~~being~~ there.
6A: Aren't you going *to* help him with that?

3 a) 'm going   b) 'm leaving   c) you will stay
d) Are you going to look / Will you look
e) 'll give   f) 's going to visit / 's visiting
g) 'll ask   h) 'll let
i) 'm going to take / 'll take / 'm taking
j) 'll show   k) 'll tell   l) 'm going to watch

4 a) I'm going to see *them* off at the station.
b) We'll get down to *it* as soon as possible.
c) We'll burn *it* down when the revolution
comes.
d) Are you looking forward to *it*?
e) Do you think we'll run out of *them*?
f) He felt he'd let *them* down when he failed his
exams.
g) Let's put *it* off until next week.
h) I hope I don't run into *them* again.

5 a) doing b) trying c) prefer d) nothing
   e) do f) would g) going h) could

6 The order is: a), d), g), b), c), f), h), e)

Vocabulary

1 *Across* 1 up 5 go 6 made 8 took 10 gets
   11 went 12 into 15 off
   Down 2 plans 3 to 4 back 5 get 7 seen
   9 over 13 to 14 of

2 a) 6 false impression
   b) 1 neighbouring communities
   c) 2 traditional dress d) 8 prime minister
   e) 5 security guard f) 3 wedding anniversary
   g) 9 train strike h) 7 waste material
   i) 4 public holiday

3 a) intention b) occasionally c) behaviour
   d) explosive(s) e) agreement f) relationship
   g) decorative h) preparations

Reading

1 a) 2, 4 b) 1 c) 3 d) 1 e) 2 f) 4 g) 2
   h) 4

2 a) bear b) snail c) ostrich d) skeleton
   e) coffin f) fireworks g) tombstone

Writing

2 Sentences 2, 7 and 9 are in the wrong letters.

4 a) I'd like to apologise for … A
   b) Can you ever forgive me for …? A
   c) You can't imagine how pleased I was to … T
   d) I'll always remember … T
   e) You must forgive me for … A
   f) I'm awfully sorry about … A
   g) I was so happy to … T
   h) It was just what I … T
   i) I wish I hadn't … A
   j) I didn't mean to … A
   k) It was really kind of you to … T

8 Review

Grammar

1 a) who b) which/that c) Since d) has
   e) have f) was g) much h) how i) was
   j) in/for/during k) are l) where m) to
   n) everything/all/what o) will

2 a) Who ~~did~~ gave you that ice-cream?
   b) What is your teacher ~~look~~ like?
   c) I have a massage from time to ~~the~~ time.
   d) I haven't been ~~going~~ to a concert for ages.
   e) They ~~have~~ lived there for six years between
      1993 and 1999.
   f) Glen has worked there since he ~~has~~ left
      college.

   g) It was a ~~very~~ brilliant film: you should go and
      see it.
   h) Have I ever ~~been~~ told you about the time I
      met Julia Roberts?
   i) Sarah Flowers is the person you want to
      speak to ~~her~~.
   j) He got up, ~~was~~ accused me of staring at him
      and walked out.
   k) The Pope is going to ~~be~~ visit Moscow.
   l) This year's Oscar was ~~being~~ won by the latest
      Spielberg film.
   m) Are you ~~going~~ doing anything interesting
      tonight?
   n) Next time I ~~will~~ see him, I'll tell him what I
      think.

3 a) normally b) drunk c) annoying
   d) travelling e) specialises f) privacy
   g) permission h) intention(s) i) destruction
   j) punishment

4 a) I haven't been to the cinema for ages.
   b) She has known him since they were students.
   c) She has never done a bungee jump before.
   d) He has lost his keys.
   e) The sun was shining when they set off.
   f) The boy, whose parents were ill, went to stay
      with his aunt.
   g) The police arrested a friend of mine last week.
   h) Photographs must not be taken here.
   i) I am going to see / I am seeing my parents at
      the weekend.
   j) I'll have / I'd like salmon and a green salad.

5 a) 2 b) 3 c) 5 d) 7 e) 10 f) 1 g) 6
   h) 8 i) 9 j) 4

Pronunciation

1 a) cost b) some c) cool d) third e) lived
   f) meant g) least

2 silent B bomb, comb, tomb
   silent T castle, listen, whistle
   silent L folk, talk, walk
   silent W wrap, written, wrong

Vocabulary

1 a) took b) terrible c) boring d) avoid
   e) robbed f) studies g) fun h) absolutely
   i) leave j) sensitive

2 a) spent b) did c) had d) made e) took
   f) put g) got h) went

3 a) up, on b) by, with c) in, at d) to, without
   e) up, on f) out, in

4 a) happy note b) previous engagement
   c) close friend d) mock exam e) short notice
   f) high speed g) full moon h) separate ways
   i) fancy dress j) private life

9 Soap

Quotations

a) family b) mother-in-law c) grandfather
d) mother

Grammar

1 a) 4 b) 1 c) 5 d) 3 e) 1 f) 2 g) 4

2 a) it was too late to cancel the wedding.
   b) Carmen was still going out with John.
   c) there was something she should know.
   d) the speech had gone really badly.
   e) they had been holding hands.
   f) they had had a terrible day.
   g) she would never speak to him again.
   h) she had (got) a problem (that) she wanted to discuss.

3 asked, told, asked, admitted, said, thought, explained, asked, insisted, asked, was wondering, suggested, pointed out

4 *Suggested answers*
   a) Daniel asked (her) if something had happened.
   b) Katy explained that she had (just) realised (that) she didn't love him.
   c) Daniel suggested that she might change her mind again.
   d) Katy insisted that it was over (for ever).
   e) Daniel asked (her) what John's reaction had been.
   f) Katy admitted that she hadn't told him yet and said that she was going to tell him later.
   g) Daniel pointed out that she couldn't really say that it was all over if she hadn't told him.

5 a) Rose ~~told~~ *said* that there was something going on between Charlie and Clare.
   b) Ella pointed out that Clare ~~she~~ was married to Dave.
   c) Rose said that lots of married people ~~do~~ have affairs.
   d) Ella asked her how she ~~did know~~ *knew*.
   e) She replied ~~her~~ that she had heard them talking on the phone.
   f) Charlie asked Clare if ~~could he~~ *he could* come and see her.
   g) Rose said that she ~~have~~ *had* got an idea.
   h) Ella asked her what ~~was it~~ *it was*.

6 a) will have found b) will be living
   c) will have d) will have discovered
   e) won't have f) will be living g) will have
   h) will not be eating

Listening and reading

1 a) F b) F c) F d) T e) F f) T g) F
   h) T i) T

Vocabulary

1 a) told b) tell c) say d) said/say
   e) told f) say g) say h) tell i) tell, told

2 Amy and Mark <u>are going through</u> a hard time at the moment. Mark <u>has been kicked out of</u> his job, and they <u>are running out of</u> money because they have just bought a new house. They <u>were counting on</u> Amy's step-father, Max, to help them financially, but he said he had a cashflow problem. They were going to have a party to celebrate Amy's birthday, but they <u>called it off</u> when they realised how much it would cost. Then, a week ago, Mark <u>ran into</u> Sonia, who he used to <u>go out with</u>. When he told Amy, she was furious, and they argued about it. It took two days for them to <u>make up</u>.

   a) to run into b) to call off c) to run out of
   d) to make up e) to be kicked out of
   f) to count on g) to go out with

3 1 niece 2 single 3 cosmetics 4 twins
   5 widow 6 predict 7 son-in-law 8 cousin
   9 retire

4 a) run b) negotiate c) signed d) go
   e) suffering f) affect g) have h) take
   i) leave j) mind

Writing

2 interests d) films b) music a)
   current work f) health e) family c)

Pronunciation

1 /s/: clocks, cosmetics, students, minutes, months, shops, trips, weeks
   /z/: birds, days, daughters, friends, jobs, lessons, twins, scales

2 /s/: crisis, discuss, increased, closest, question
   /z/: designer, exercise, cosmetics, organise, pleasant, present, Thursday

---

10 Time

Time idioms

a) day ... night
   If you call it a day, you decide to stop doing something and finish it later. If you have an early night, you go to bed early.
b) minute
   Something that is up-to-the-minute contains the latest information.
c) hour ... day
   If something happens at the eleventh hour, it happens just before it is too late. If someone or something saves the day, they end a bad situation.

Grammar

1   at about half past eight
at around three o'clock
at the start of the week
in the early hours of the morning
in the middle of the afternoon
in the middle of the day
just after you have had lunch
on New Year's Day
on the fourth of July

2   *Students' own answers*

3   a)   1 have   2 can   3 allowed   4 must
b)   1 must   2 have   3 supposed   4 should
     5 got
c)   1 can't   2 have   3 allowed   4 supposed

4   a)   1   We must be in good physical condition.
     2   You have got to follow orders all the time.
     3   You are allowed to live with your family
         when you're promoted.
     4   You don't have to wear uniform in the
         evenings.
b)   1   You don't have to have any special
         training.
     2   You are supposed to agree with
         everything your leader says.
     3   You should be well dressed.
     4   You have got to be very ambitious.

5   a)   museum attendant – Exercise 3 c)
b)   politician – Exercise 4 b)
c)   taxi driver – Exercise 3 a)
d)   footballer – Exercise 3 b)
e)   soldier – Exercise 4 a)

Listening

1

	1	2	3	4	5	6	7	8	9	10	11	12
AM			a			e / f						
	1	2	3	4	5	6	7	8	9	10	11	12
PM		g		h		b		c		d		

2   early hours   night shift   alcoholic drinks
strictly speaking   blood cells   immune system
contagious diseases   physical exercise

Vocabulary

1   a) time   b) time   c) times   d) times
e) time   f) time   g) times   h) times
i) time   j) time

2   a) client   b) flexible   c) deadline   d) colleague
e) database   f) interview   g) executive
h) premises   i) applicant

3   a) overnight bag   b) action plan
c) model agency   d) working week
e) lunch hour   f) casual clothes

Pronunciation

1   a) 6th 6 16th   b) 33rd 13th 30th
c) 945 9.45 9.45 (time)   d) 1.988 1988 1,988

Writing

2   The correct order is 3, 2, 5, 4, 1.

3   a) in, to, in   b) At, as, at   c) As, from
d) in, to   e) to, for   f) for, at

---

11 Journey

Travel expressions

a) 6   b) 3   c) 1   d) 2   e) 5   f) 4

Grammar

1   A Venezuela   B Brazil   C Cuba

2   Country A   a) can't   b) might   c) suppose
d) definitely
Country B   a) certainly   b) can't   c) could
d) must

4   a) 6   b) 5   c) 2   d) 4   e) 1   f) 7   g) 3   h) 8

5   a) had already visited   b) thought   c) went
d) had decided   e) became   f) had invited
g) met   h) had never been   i) had known

6   a) would   b) would   c) had   d) would
e) had   f) would   g) would

7   P: c) e) g) h)   I: a) b) d) f)

Listening

1   ☹ Speakers 1, 3, 4   ☺ Speakers 2, 5, 6

2   entertainment 2, food 5, hotel 3, journey 4, price
1, weather 6

3   1   a F   b T
2   a T   b T
3   a T   b F
4   a F   b T
5   a T   b T
6   a F   b F

Vocabulary

1 a) engagement b) departure c) boredom
    d) friendly e) meaningless f) amazement
    g) emotionally h) connecting

2 a) luck b) dream c) break d) price e) eye
    f) board g) head h) never i) stretch j) deal

3 *Words connected with cities:* capital, traffic, jams
    Words connected with the seaside: beach, sandy, surf,
    waves
    Words connected with air travel: airport, aisle, flight,
    check-in
    Words connected with the countryside: hills, peaks,
    fields
    Adjectives to describe views: breath-taking,
    gorgeous, picturesque, spectacular

---

12 Basics

Basic idioms

a) food for thought b) lose sleep over it
c) put to sleep d) eating out of your hand
e) home game f) home and dry
g) home from home

Grammar

1 a) a b) a c) an d) an e) a f) an g) an
    h) a i) an j) an k) an l) a m) an n) a
    If you put *an* before the word, *the* will be
    pronounced /ðiː/.
    If you put *a* before the word, *the* will be
    pronounced /ðə/.

2 a) sardines b) tuna c) garlic d) sauce
    e) fish f) mussels g) seafood h) lamb
    i) vegetables j) meat k) dishes l) beers
    m) olives n) sandwiches o) glasses p) cod

3 a) comes b) cost c) was d) is e) is
    f) are g) was h) live

4 a) the b) a c) the d) the e) a f) –
    g) the h) – i) the j) the k) the l) a

5 a) few b) some c) any d) no e) much
    f) many g) little h) couple i) bit

6 a) We had soup as a starter and it wasn't hot
        enough.
    b) There wasn't *enough* bread and the waiter
        wouldn't bring us any more.
    c) There was *too* much salt in the pasta.
    d) I asked for the meat to be not *too* well-done ...
    e) ... but when it came, it wasn't cooked *enough*
        – it was almost raw.
    f) They had put far *too* much garlic in the sauce.
    g) The bill was much *too* expensive.
    h) We didn't have *enough* money to pay.

Pronunciation

1 cu<u>sh</u>ions   informa<u>ti</u>on
    di<u>sh</u>es   ma<u>chi</u>ne
    Engli<u>sh</u>   mu<u>sh</u>room
    expre<u>ssi</u>on   reserva<u>ti</u>on
    <u>sh</u>ould   spa<u>ci</u>ous
    <u>s</u>ugar   wa<u>sh</u>ing

Reading

1 a) 1 b) 6 c) 5 d) 3 e) 4 f) 2

2 a) there's a good chance b) curious
    c) any number of d) it is available
    e) set you back f) frankly g) touch the stuff
    h) it couldn't really fail to i) trendy
    j) refers to

Vocabulary

1 a) organic b) strong c) draught
    d) wholemeal e) spicy f) roast
    g) full-bodied h) mild

2 *Meat and fish*
    hake lobster prawns sausages turkey
    veal
    Vegetables
    aubergine beans cauliflower celery garlic
    leek lettuce
    Fruit
    figs grapefruit lime peach plum
    raspberries

3 a) 2 b) 10 c) 7 d) 4 e) 3 f) 9 g) 1
    h) 5 i) 8 j) 6

4 a) nightmares b) nap c) snoring d) insomnia
    e) yawning f) alarm clock g) lie-in
    h) early bird

Writing

1 a) 10 b) 8 c) 1 d) 9 e) 2 f) 4 g) 7 h) 6
    i) 5 j) 3

---

13 Communication

Communicative idioms

a) It is on the tip of my tongue.
b) I was completely lost for words.
c) I don't know what you are on about. (NB this is
    very direct!)
d) You took the words out of my mouth.
e) You can say that again.
f) You are talking through your hat.

a) 3 b) 6 c) 2 d) 4 e) 1 f) 5

Grammar

1 a) 1 unless 2 When 3 If
b) 1 if 2 when 3 unless
c) 1 when 2 If 3 unless
d) 1 when 2 if 3 unless

2 a) Unless you hurry up, we'll never get there on time.
We'll never get there on time unless you hurry up.
b) Unless you tell me what the problem is, I can't help you.
I can't help you unless you tell me what the problem is.
c) They have decided to dismiss her unless she resigns from the post.
d) We usually go out on Saturday night unless we have to work.
Unless we have to work, we usually go out on Saturday night.
e) Unless you try a bit harder, you'll never find a job.
You'll never find a job unless you try a bit harder.
f) Don't buy it unless you've got enough money.
Unless you've got enough money, don't buy it.

3 a) I'll ask him to switch it off if it rings again.
b) I'll speak to him if you like.
c) What shall we do if he refuses?
d) If he says 'no' we'll have to change seats.
e) Why doesn't / won't he move if he is causing a problem?
f) Why did he come to the cinema if he wants / wanted to speak to his friends?
g) If he has (got) so many friends why is he sitting all alone?
h) If I ever buy a mobile phone, I'll switch it off in the cinema.

4 a) have b) will never get c) won't have
d) make / have made e) haven't made
f) start g) will you change
h) didn't you phone

5 a) also b) unless c) can d) if e) have
f) will g) until h) especially i) manage
j) wanted k) don't l) when

Listening and reading

1 Message 1 a train service
Message 2 a castle
Message 3 a theatre
Message 4 a language school
Message 5 an art gallery

2 and 3

1 Thank you *for* calling *****, the high speed passenger service. Please choose *from* one of the following four options. To listen to our talking timetable, press 0. To make a booking, press 1. If you are calling *about* an existing booking, press 2. For other enquiries, press 3.

2 This is *****. I'm sorry, but the switchboard is now closed. If you wish to speak *to* an operator, please call this number *between 8 am and 5.30* pm Monday to Friday. The switchboard is not open *at* the weekends or bank holidays. If you wish to listen to recorded information on *****'s opening times and admission prices, please call *020 7680 9004. I repeat 020 7680 9004*.

3 This is the box office at the *****. All our lines are busy *at* the moment. Your call will be answered as soon as possible. We are booking *by* phone and *in* person for performances to *17th* July. If you have a touch-tone phone and you would like to hear information on this week's performances and ticket availability, press 1.

4 Thank you for calling *****. Staff will be available to take your enquiry *at* the following times. *On* Mondays and Fridays, staff will be available from 9 am to *7.15* pm. From Tuesday to Thursday, staff will be available from 9 am to 9 pm. The school will also be open on certain *Saturdays* when you will receive a limited information service. Should you call *outside* these times, please leave a clear message after the tone.

5 Hello. You have reached the ***** answering service. I'm afraid that all our operators are busy *at* the moment. For information *about* our current exhibition and *for* full details about Joe Cook, our artist of the *week*, please press 'one'. For all other enquiries, please hold until an operator becomes available.

Vocabulary

1 a) – Sue? Hi, it's Christine. How are you doing?
– Oh, hi. Listen, do you mind if I call you back? I can't speak right now.
– Sure. I'll be in all afternoon.
– OK. I'll speak to you in half an hour or so.

b) – 734 4702.
– Hello. Could I speak to Helen, please?
– Is that David? It's Jane here.
– Oh, hi, Jane. Is Helen there?
– Yeah, hang on. I'll go and get her.

c) – Accounts department. Can I help you?
– Yes, could I speak to Mr Read, please?
– I'm afraid he's not available at the moment. Can I take a message?
– Yes, could you tell him that John Lawson called?
– Certainly, Mr Lawson.

d) – Macmillan Oxford, good afternoon. Can I
help you?
– Yes, could I speak to Katy Wright, please?
– I'll put you through. I'm afraid her line's
busy. Would you like to leave a message?
– Yes. Could you say that Markella
returned her call?
– Yes, of course. Could you spell that for
me, please?

2 a) do b) make c) do d) do e) make
f) make g) make h) make i) do j) do

1 make your mind up 2 do the washing
3 make a suggestion 4 do your homework
5 do your best 6 do the accounts
7 make the bed 8 make a lot of noise
9 do some work 10 make a good impression

3 a) at b) up c) on d) of e) with f) about
g) on h) for i) over j) about

Writing

1 a few times – on a number of occasions
about – with reference to
We noticed – It has come to our attention
You know – You will be aware
fix a date – make an appointment
have a chat with – speak to
give us a call – contact us
as soon as you can – at your earliest convenience
Love – Yours sincerely

2 a) B b) M c) B d) M e) B f) M g) B
h) M i) B j) B k) M l) B m) M n) M

---

14 Style

Proverbs

The proverb which has a different meaning is 'Every
shoe does not fit every foot', which means that people
are different. All the others are about the superficiality
of appearances.

Grammar

1 a) would look b) were/was c) would wear
d) bought e) had f) had g) would mind
h) asked i) asked j) could postpone
k) would probably say l) would want

2 *Possible answers*
a) might like you.
b) would feel better about yourself.
c) you went out more often.
d) used chatlines on the Internet.
e) could afford to go out.
f) got your modem mended.
g) wouldn't walk away.
h) your trainers weren't so smelly.

3 a) would b) wouldn't c) looked d) was
e) wasn't f) was g) had h) wasn't
i) could tell j) would kiss

4 a) horrible, knee-length, fake leather *motorcycle*
boots
b) a pair of *ridiculous* baggy tartan trousers
c) an *ancient* snakeskin cowboy belt
d) an old-fashioned, dark brown *nylon* shirt
e) an amazing *flowery* silk tie
f) an extraordinary, full-length *purple* velvet coat
g) an enormous black and white checked *baseball*
cap

Listening

1 c)

2 a) T b) F c) T d) F e) F f) F g) F h) T

Vocabulary

1 *Clothes*
belt boots cap cardigan coat jacket scarf
suit sweatshirt underwear waistcoat
Materials
cashmere cord denim fur leather nylon
silk velvet wool

2 a) 4 b) 5 c) 2 d) 1 e) 6 f) 3

3 A has a pierced nose, B hasn't.
A is clean-shaved, B has stubble.
A has a scar on his cheek, B has a scar on his
forehead.
B has thick eyebrows, A hasn't.
B has buckles on his shoes, A has laces.
A has a zip on his jacket, B has buttons.

Writing

1 appearance *paragraph 1*
clothes *paragraph 3*
interests *paragraph 4*
personality *paragraph 2*

2 My little niece, Lou, is eight years old, and is the
spitting image of my sister. I have a photo of my
sister when she was the same age and you can't
tell them apart. She's got straight fair hair with a
fringe, and the first thing you notice about her are
her bright blue eyes. She's got a lovely smile.
*When she finds something funny, it's impossible not to
smile with her.*
To begin with she seems quite shy, but when she
gets to know you, she never stops talking. Her
teachers say she's a real chatterbox. She
particularly likes telling jokes, and when she is
with her friends they never stop laughing. She's
also very generous. *I remember one day she had to go
into hospital, and when she left she wanted to give all
her toys to the hospital for the other kids.*

She used to like wearing flowery dresses, but she's gone off them now because she thinks they are too 'girlish'. *Every now and then, she'll wear a dress, but it has to be black and 'grown-up'.* But most of the time, she just puts on jeans and a T-shirt. If you saw her in the street, you would probably think she was two or three years older.

She's really into girl groups like All Saints. *When she's not at school, she has always got her Walkman with her.* She sings at the top of her voice because she keeps forgetting that everyone can hear her. The only problem with this is that she can't sing to save her life.

3 a) A b) P c) P d) A/C e) C f) A g) P h) C i) A

Pronunciation

1 Ooo: casual, glamorous, probably, gallery, obvious
oOo: designer, romantic, commercial, expensive, attractive

---

15 Age

Grammar

1 a) I wish the police hadn't seen me.
b) I wish I hadn't drunk so much at the party.
c) I wish I had left my car at the party.
d) I wish I had asked someone to give me a lift home.
e) I wish I had called a taxi.
f) I wish I hadn't chosen such a stupid costume.
g) I wish I had changed before leaving the party.
h) I wish I hadn't gone to the party.

2 a) hadn't gone, wouldn't be
b) had thought, would have chosen
c) would have left, had chosen
d) had felt, would have drunk
e) would still be, had taken
f) hadn't jumped, wouldn't have stopped
g) would be, hadn't been
h) had happened, would feel/would be feeling

3 a) ... why you are wearing those clothes?
b) ... what sort of party it was?
c) ... if/whether you often dress like that?
d) ... if/whether you have (got) any other clothes?
e) ... what time you left the party?
f) ... if/whether you knew you had drunk too much?
g) ... if/whether you have ever been arrested before?
h) ... if/whether your wife knows where you were?

4 a) would need b) wouldn't have overslept
c) wouldn't have arrived d) weren't/wasn't
e) wouldn't be f) hadn't eaten

5 a) U b) R c) U d) R e) U f) R

Listening

1 picture C

2 He talks about: a, d, e, f, g, i, l, n, o

Vocabulary

1 a) ambitious b) sane c) financial
d) disastrous e) anxious f) enjoyable
g) desperate h) adventurous

2 a) take b) pass c) lost d) made e) having
f) go g) got h) wear

3 a) bean b) beg c) broke d) counter
e) dyes f) fall g) fun h) liar i) lick j) oven
k) tin l) tongue m) trolley

Writing

1 The order is a, f, d, c, e, b.

---

16 Review

Grammar

1 a) The b) are c) many d) can e) should
f) see/spot g) can/could/may/might
h) needed/needs i) when j) will k) an/one
l) was m) would/could n) if o) enough

2 a) By this time next week, we will have been ~~being~~ here for over a year.
b) He told ~~to~~ me you were having problems with your computer.
c) You don't have ~~got~~ to do that if you don't want to.
d) We ~~can~~ are allowed to wear anything we like.
e) I'd ~~have~~ finished dinner by the time she arrived.
f) It might not ~~to~~ be very hot when you arrive.
g) There were ~~not~~ hardly any people in the restaurant.
h) We're going on holiday to ~~the~~ France next year.
i) If you ~~will~~ arrive early, give me a call.
j) Don't look at the answers unless you ~~don't~~ find it impossible without them.
k) I wish I ~~didn't~~ had a bit more money.
l) Have you ever had your hair ~~been~~ dyed?
m) If you ask me, your hair is too ~~much~~ short.
n) We wouldn't be lost if you ~~could~~ had brought a map.

3 a) speech b) violence c) thirtieth
d) freedom e) Belgian f) unexpectedly
g) unhealthy h) sharpened

4 a) She asked me if had seen the latest episode of *Pacific Heights*.

b) By the end of the year, I will have studied English for five years.

c) You don't have to / need to answer every question.

d) What are we supposed to do if we don't understand?

e) You must speak English well after your course.

f) Unless you are interested, you probably won't learn much.

g) I wish I hadn't had my nose pierced.

h) 'If I were you, I'd find a new hairdresser,' she advised me / said to me.

i) If we had not left early we would have missed the train.

j) If only I had remembered his name.

5 a) 2 b) 1 c) 5 d) 10 e) 6 f) 7 g) 8 h) 4
i) 9 j) 3

Pronunciation

1 a) /j/ b) /w/ c) /j/ d) /w/ e) /j/
f) /j/ g) /j/ h) /w/ i) /w/ j) /w/

2 a), c), f) and h) are complete.

b) 1

d) 2

e) 3

g) 4

i) 5

Vocabulary

1 a) expect b) mid c) suit d) former
e) rather f) deny g) arguments h) to break
i) several j) remind

2 a) got b) did c) held d) served e) had
f) put g) made h) said

3 a) for, in b) on, on c) up, at d) in/near, to
e) to, on f) through, on g) of, up h) off, up

4 a) plain chocolate

b) good looks

c) opposite sex

d) constant pressure

e) strong coffee

f) standard practice

g) second thoughts

h) higher education

i) nuclear family

j) reasonable price